Philip Carter is a Yorkshire estimator and a Justice of the Peace. He is Puzzle Editor of *Enigmasig*, the magazine for the Mensa Puzzle Special Interest Group.

Ken Russell is a former London surveyor who lives in Kent. He is the Puzzle Editor of *Mensa*, a magazine issued free each month to Mensa's 43,000 UK members.

Also by Philip Carter and Ken Russell:

THE MENSA PUZZLE BOOK
THE MENSA PUZZLE BOOK 2
THE MENSA PUZZLE BOOK 3
THE JUNIOR MENSA PUZZLE BOOK
THE IQ TEST BOOK
CLASSIC PUZZLES
MENSA BOOK OF ENIGMAGRAMS
THE MENSA CHALLENGE
THE MENSA GENERAL KNOWLEDGE QUIZ BOOK

General Knowledge Quiz Book 2

For the making of Masterminds

By the Mensa Puzzle Experts

Philip Carter
Ken Russell

WARNER BOOKS

A *Warner* Book

First published in Great Britain in 1994
by Warner Books

Copyright © 1994 by Philip Carter and Ken Russell

The moral right of the author has been asserted.

A CIP catalogue record for this book is
available from the British Library.

ISBN 0 7515 0754 7

Typeset by Solidus (Bristol) Limited
Printed and bound in Great Britain by
Clays Ltd, St. Ives plc

Warner Books
A Division of
Little, Brown and Company (UK)
Brettenham House
Lancaster Place
London WC2E 7EN

Author's Note

This book is dedicated to our wives, both named Barbara, who have given us their support and encouragement in our endeavour to compile new and interesting questions, and have checked out the answers.

We also wish to acknowledge the assistance and advice given to us by Victor Serebriakoff, the International President of Mensa, who is a great puzzle innovator. We are indebted too to Harold Gale, the Mensa Chief Executive, a prolific puzzle composer.

What is Mensa?

Mensa is a unique society. It is, basically, a social club – but a social club different from others. The only qualification for membership is a high score on an intelligence test. One person in fifty should qualify for membership; these people will come from all walks of life and have a wide variety of interests and occupations.

Mensa is the Latin word for table: we are a round-table society where no one has special precedence. We fill a void for many intelligent people otherwise cut off from contact with other good minds – contact that is important to them, but elusive in modern society. Besides being an origin of many new friendships, we provide members with a receptive but critical audience on which to try out new ideas.

Mensa is protean: its most visible feature is its diversity. It crosses the often artificial barriers which separate people from each other. It recruits, not like other societies by persuading people to think as they do, or by searching for a particularly narrow common interest, but by scientifically selecting people who are able to think for themselves. Yet, although there appears little common ground and little surface agreement between members, we find there is an underlying unity which gives an unexpected strength to the society.

Mensa has three aims: social contact between intelligent people; research in psychology and the social sciences; and the identification and fostering of human intelligence. Mensa is an international society; it has more than 110,000 members. We have members of almost every occupation – business people, clerks, doctors, editors, factory workers, farm labourers, housewives, lawyers, police officers, politicians, soldiers, scientists, students, teachers – and of almost every age.

Enquiries and applications to:

Mensa
FREEPOST
Wolverhampton WV2 1BR

Mensa International
15 The Ivories
6–8 Northampton Street
London N1 2HV

Each answer begins with the letter on the right: each dot stands for a letter. Scoring for each quiz is included in the answers section.

Scoring for quiz one as follows:

10–12	Fair
13–17	Good
18–21	Very good
22–24	Excellent

Each subsequent quiz progressively increases in difficulty and scoring is gradually adjusted accordingly.

The quizzes are designed to test both your word power and general knowledge. The odd numbered quizzes are mainly a test of general knowledge with an element of word power and the even numbered quizzes are mainly a test of word power with an element of general knowledge.

1   The fruit of the oak tree.   A . . . .

2   Which city would you associate with
the Reichstag?   B . . . . .

3   1943 classic film starring Humphrey
Bogart and Ingrid Bergman.   C . . . .

4   She betrayed Samson by cutting off his
hair.   D . . . . . .

5   Creature known as a moose in North
America.   E . .

6   What was the nickname of the
American jazz pianist and composer
Thomas Wright Waller?   F . . .

7   What, collectively, were Spike Milligan,
Peter Sellers, Harry Secombe and Michael
Bentine?   G . . . .

8   The name in Scotland for New Year's
Eve.   H . . . .

9   In the USA it is the 'Gem State'.   I . . . .

10   What word goes before baby, bag and
bean?   J . . . .

11   Where, in Surrey, are the Royal
Botanical Gardens?   K . .

12   Buddhist monk in Tibet or Mongolia.   L . . .

13   The Roman God of War.   M . . .

14   British Admiral who fell in love with
Emma, Lady Hamilton.   N . . . . .

15   Unit of weight, the sixteenth part of a
pound.   O . . . .

16   Alexandrite, moonstone and which
other gemstone are associated with the
month of June?   P . . . .

17 The most powerful piece in chess. Q . . . .

18 Who did the sparrow kill in the nursery rhyme? R . . . .

19 Whose motto is 'Be prepared'? S . . . . .

20 Another name for a tornado in the USA. T . . . . . .

21 A person in business or insurance who guarantees payment. U . . . .

22 Entertainment art practised by such performers as Peter Brough, Keith Harris and Ray Allen. V . . . .

23 In which Belgian town was Napoleon defeated in 1815? W . . . .

24 What are Finn, Flying Dutchman and International Tornado classes of? Y . . . .

TWO

1 Lady Superior in an Abbey. A . . . . .
2 Narrative poem which is sung. B . . . . .
3 Inventor of the revolver. C . . .
4 Lifeboat supports. D . . . . .
5 Pressed yellow cheese. E . . .
6 A ballroom dance. F . . . . . .
7 Plucked string instrument. G . . . . .
8 Group of giraffes. H . . .
9 Where were the Hanging Gardens of Babylon? I . . .
10 Big sea battle of 1916. J . . . . . .
11 Currency of Laos. K . .
12 In which museum is the *Mona Lisa*? L . . . . .

13	Inventor of telegraphic code.	M ....
14	Feeling of sickness.	N .....
15	City in Canada.	O .....
16	Which city was destroyed by Mt. Vesuvius?	P ......
17	A fast fox-trot.	Q ....
18	Republic of Central Africa.	R ....
19	Largest port in South East Asia.	S ....
20	Male head-dress.	T .....
21	Group of ravens.	U ....
22	Fine parchment made of calf skin.	V ....
23	Inventor of the fountain-pen.	W ....
24	A ship's jolly-boat.	Y ...

THREE

1	The crime of a pyromaniac.	A ....
2	What type of vessels were the Japanese *Musashi* and *Yamato*, both sunk in World War II?	B ....
3	The Roman God of Love.	C ....
4	Which Saint's Day falls on 1st March?	D ....
5	King Arthur's sword.	E ....
6	What is the value of the brown ball in snooker?	F ...
7	What word comes before widow, court and land?	G ....
8	Forecast based on the relative positioning of the stars and planets at a given moment.	H ....
9	Which Russian name is the equivalent of John?	I ...

10 A type of puzzle.   J . . . . .

11 What is the name of Kenya's highest mountain?   K . . . .

12 A fast of forty days from Ash Wednesday to Easter Eve.   L . . .

13 Centipede-like creature having two pairs of legs on each segment.   M . . . .

14 Seven-a-side court game for women.   N . . . . . .

15 What word comes before rags, blue and shoe?   O . . . . .

16 What is meant by the mathematical symbol '||'?   P . . . .

17 Measure equal to 2 pints or approximately 1.1 litres.   Q . . . .

18 An arc of light comprising the spectral colours.   R . . . . . .

19 The national emblem of Ireland.   S . . . .

20 Dynasty which ended with the death of Elizabeth I in 1603.   T . . . .

21 'The Beehive State' is the nickname for which American state?   U . . .

22 The flesh of the deer as food.   V . . . . . .

23 What type of instruments are the piccolo, flute, oboe, clarinet, cor anglais and bassoon?   W . . . .

24 Another name for the 'Abominable Snowman'.   Y . . .

FOUR

1 The highest point.   A . . .

2 A Spanish dance.   B . . . . .

3	Group of actors.	C . . . . . .
4	Extinct bird.	D . . .
5	Large Australian flightless bird.	E . .
6	Nautical measure.	F . . . . .
7	Inventor of the safety razor.	G . . . .
8	Killing of human beings.	H . . . .
9	Charge with a crime.	I . . . . . .
10	Combat between mounted lancers.	J . . . .
11	Which British film star of the 30s and 40s was born William Pratt?	K . . . . . .
12	Form of prayer.	L . . . . .
13	Which country was conquered by Cortes?	M . . . . .
14	Large group of people.	N . . . . .
15	Marsupial type of animal.	O . . . . . .
16	Currency of Mexico.	P . . .
17	A monocle with a handle.	Q . . .
18	Pinkish coloured table wine.	R . . .
19	The highest female voice.	S . . . . . .
20	Male garment in Ancient Rome.	T . . .
21	Milk-secreting organ of a cow.	U . . . .
22	A blood feud.	V . . . .
23	Wire hoops used in croquet.	W . . . . . .
24	Currency of Japan.	Y . .

FIVE

| 1 | Portable organ-type musical instrument. | A . . . . |
| 2 | John, Paul, Ringo and George collectively. | B . . . . . . |

3 What is the English name of the constellation in the night sky which bears the Latin name 'Cancer'? C . . .

4 US term for a bowler hat. D . . . .

5 Green transparent variety of beryl. E . . . . . .

6 Old British two-shilling coin. F . . . . .

7 Who did Queen Victoria say spoke to her as if she were a public meeting? G . . . .

8 American lyricist who with Richard Rogers wrote *Oklahoma*, *South Pacific* and *The Sound of Music*. H . . . .

9 Large island in the North Atlantic. I . . . . . .

10 What female Christian name means 'Jewess' in Hebrew? J . . . . .

11 Who said, 'As a free man, I take pride in the words *ich bin ein Berliner*'? K . . . . . .

12 What word is connected with torch song, serenade and billet-doux? L . . .

13 Who was the incurable optimist in Dickens' novel *David Copperfield*? M . . . .

14 European kingdom, occupying the west part of the Scandinavian peninsula. N . . . . .

15 A large passenger vehicle. O . . . . . .

16 What sord of words are repaper, gag and level? P . . . .

17 What word means a shallow mine and an object of pursuit? Q . . . . .

18 The second largest land animal (after the elephant). R . . . .

19 Which Saint's Day falls on 26th December? S . . . . . .

20 Set of three related works of literature by the same author. T . . . . . .

21 In Scotland, what are Heriot Watt and St Andrews? U . . . .

22 Who composed '*La Traviata*'? V . . . .

23 What is the largest lake in England? W . . . .

24 What is the method of photocopying devised in the 1930s by US physicist Chester F . Carlson? X . . . .

SIX

---

1   Cutting tool with arched blade. A . . .

2   Group of masons. B . . . .

3   Long pole used in Highland Games. C . . . .

4   A loose woman. D . . .

5   Duelling sword. E . . .

6   Inventor of bifocal lens. F . . . .

7   Inventor of vulcanised rubber. G . . . .

8   Another name for a mouth organ. H . . . .

9   A fire on the hearth. I . . . .

10 Carnivorous member of the dog family. J . . . . .

11 South Africa Bantu people. K . . . . .

12 Handle of opera glasses. L . . . .

13 English folk dance. M . . . . .

14 Study of new words. N . . . . . .

15 Kind of China tea. O . . . . .

16 Inventor of the adding machine. P . . . . .

17 Another name for mercury. Q . . . .

18 Currency of Namibia. R . . .

19 River on which Paris stands. S . . . .

20 Fly that causes sleeping sickness. T . . . . .

21	Rain gauge.	U . . . .
22	What male forename means conqueror?	V . . . . . .
23	Group of swans.	W . . . .
24	A youngster.	Y . . . . . .

SEVEN

1	In Greek mythology, who fell in love with Aphrodite?	A . . . . .
2	Who wrote *Peter Pan*?	B . . . . .
3	What is the name of the quarter note ♩?	C . . . .
4	In what type of auction is the price progressively lowered until a buyer accepts?	D . . . .
5	Who invented the electric light bulb?	E . . . . .
6	What word is fax an abbreviation of?	F . . . .
7	The stars Castor and Pollux are in which constellation?	G . . . . .
8	Fibre-tipped pen with wide nib for drawing over words in a text to draw attention to them.	H . . . .
9	What sort of board is an autocue said to be?	I . . . .
10	Of where is St Helier the capital?	J . . . . .
11	What does a cutler make, sell or repair?	K . . . . .
12	American heavyweight boxer known as 'The Brown Bomber'.	L . . . .
13	Who in Genesis 5:27 was said to have lived for 969 years?	M . . . .
14	In the USA it is the 'Cornhusker State'.	N . . . .
15	The fruit of the citrus aurantium.	O . . . . .

16 Sports contest consisting of running, riding, fencing, swimming and pistol shooting.   P . . . .

17 Any four-footed animal.   Q . . . .

18 Russian dynasty of 17th–20th century.   R . . . . . .

19 Old British £1 coin.   S . . . .

20 Cistercian order of monks noted for their austerity and vow of silence.   T . . . .

21 Too deep to be measured.   U . . . .

22 Word-for-word.   V . . . .

23 Headquarters of the All-England Tennis Club.   W . . . .

24 Type of cattle native to Tibet.   Y . .

EIGHT

1   Soon after.   A . . .

2   Group of chickens.   B . . . . . .

3   Tenth part of a Roman legion.   C . . . . .

4   Currency of Greece.   D . . . . . .

5   Edible snail.   E . . . .

6   Dance from Andalusia.   F . . . .

7   Flat decked ship rowed by oars.   G . . . . .

8   Karl Marx buried in this cemetery.   H . . . .

9   A mass of cast metal.   I . . . .

10 Whirlpool in a domestic bath.   J . . . . . .

11 Small portable anchor.   K . . . .

12 What are Frisian and Romance?   L . . . .

13 Capital of Uruguay.   M . . . .

14 Greek God of Retribution.   N . . . . . .

15	Inventor of the elevator.	O . . .
16	A game played with 32 cards.	P . . . . .
17	A grain measure of 8 bushels.	Q . . . . . .
18	Killing kings.	R . . . .
19	Bird allied to the sparrow.	S . . . . .
20	Group of monkeys.	T . . . .
21	Long loose overcoat.	U . . . . .
22	Parish priest or minister.	V . . . .
23	Another name for Tungsten.	W . . . . . .
24	Yorkshire terrier.	Y . . . . .

NINE

1	Of what is genealogy the study?	A . . . .
2	What was the nickname of the straightfaced American comedian Joseph Francis Keaton?	B . . . . .
3	Who is the patron saint of motorists?	C . . . .
4	One 360th part of a complete revolution.	D . . . . .
5	It can be annular, solar or total.	E . . . . . .
6	Austrian founder of psychoanalysis.	F . . . .
7	A native of Tyneside.	G . . . . . .
8	What does the letter 'H' stand for in W.H.O.?	H . . . . .
9	The Greek letter i.	I . . .
10	In the film 'The Jazz Singer', who said, 'You ain't heard nothin' yet, folks!'	J . . . . .
11	The capital of Sudan.	K . . . .
12	Domesticated Peruvian wool-bearing animal.	L . . . .

13 The fictional inspector created by Colin Dexter. M....

14 Winner of nine singles at Wimbledon 1978–1990. N..........

15 A fertile spot in a desert. O....

16 What word is derived from 'pedestrian light controlled crossing'? P......

17 Who was the marquess who, in 1867, drew up the standard rules of boxing? Q..........

18 Substance obtained from latex-producing tropical trees. R.....

19 What is the name of the glove puppet made famous by Harry Corbett? S....

20 From what country is the Dalai Lama exiled? T....

21 Element with atomic no. 92 and symbol U. U......

22 Describes a car made before 1919. V......

23 In which London borough are the Houses of Parliament situated? W..........

24 A fungus used in the brewing and baking industries. Y....

TEN
_____

1 A fight in a public place. A.....

2 Group of directors. B....

3 A type of rabbit. C....

4 Chief magistrate of Venice. D...

5 Shield shaped. E.........

6 Drooping flowered shrub. F......

7 Inventor of machine gun. G......

8	Small hill or mound.	H . . . . . .
9	To over-run.	I . . . . .
10	Red, brown, or yellow gem.	J . . . . .
11	Austrian cataloguer of Mozart's work.	K . . . . .
12	Form on which a shoe is made.	L . . .
13	Extinct flightless bird.	M . .
14	Inventor of logarithms.	N . . . . .
15	Scapa Flow is in?	O . . . . . .
16	Piglike animal of the Americas.	P . . . . . .
17	Of the fifth degree.	Q . . . . . .
18	Another name for a rugby scrum.	R . . .
19	Group of soldiers.	S . . . .
20	Exponent of archery.	T . . . .
21	Situated beyond the sea.	U . . . .
22	South African monkey.	V . . . . .
23	Currency of Korea.	W . .
24	Chinese tree.	Y . . . .

ELEVEN

1	They sailed with Jason to find the Golden Fleece.	A . . . .
2	Who was the actress wife of Humphrey Bogart?	B . . . . .
3	Who said 'I believe it is peace for our time . . . peace with honour'?	C . . . .
4	Who invented the safety lamp formerly used by coal miners?	D . . .
5	Biblical place associated with Paradise.	E . . .

6 George Ellis described the months as
snowy, flowy, blowy, showery, flowery,
bowery, hoppy, croppy, droppy, breezy,
sneezy and ?   F . . . . .

7 What type of clubs are small choirs
which usually perform light, short musical
pieces?   G . . .

8 A suburb of Los Angeles.   H . . . .

9 What was the name of the famous radio
comedy series starring Tommy Handley?   I . . .

10 The capital of Indonesia.   J . . . . . .

11 Major diamond-mining centre in
South Africa.   K . . . .

12 A young hare.   L . . . . . .

13 Small table-top device for moving a
cursor on a VDU.   M . . . .

14 A favourite children's character
created by Enid Blyton.   N . . . .

15 What is the American for fly-over?   O . . . .

16 Element with atomic no. 19 and
symbol K.   P . . . .

17 Twenty-four sheets of paper.   Q . . . .

18 The language of the gypsies.   R . . . . .

19 Polish trade union led by Lech
Walesa.   S . . . .

20 How many years' marriage are
celebrated by a pearl anniversary?   T . . . . .

21 Pertaining to a city or town.   U . . . .

22 Jascha Heifetz was a famous one.   V . . . .

23 The Lord Chancellor's official seat in
the House of Lords.   W . . . .

24 The daughter of Princess Anne and
Mark Phillips.   Z . . .

1	Large type of terrier.	A.......
2	Collection of bread in oven.	B....
3	A grappling iron.	C.....
4	Inventor of the carburettor.	D......
5	Coarse grass.	E......
6	A complete failure.	F.....
7	A gaudy plaything.	G..-...
8	North Atlantic fish.	H......
9	A property that a body has to remain stationary or move in a straight line.	I......
10	Truculent and blinkered patriotism.	J.......
11	Movement under stimulus.	K......
12	A footman.	L.....
13	Composer of opera *Idomeneo*.	M.....
14	Deputy governor or prince mogul.	N....
15	Mix alazerin with gamboge, what colour?	O.....
16	Set of five.	P.....
17	Size of paper.	Q.....
18	Currency of Iran.	R...
19	Inventor of electric razor.	S.....
20	Group of minstrels.	T.....
21	Resembling a bear.	U.....
22	Roller-skating stadium.	V........
23	What is Cambria called today?	W....
24	Country bumpkin.	Y....

THIRTEEN

1   In Greek mythology, who was condemned by Zeus to support the heavens on his shoulders?

A . . . .

2   Unit, equivalent to eight bits, used to measure a computer's memory.

B . . .

3   Which lord, together with Howard Carter, discovered the tomb of Tutankhamen?

C . . . .

4   Street off Whitehall, London, which now contains just three of its original row of terraced houses.

D . . . . . .

5   Which British army under the command of Montgomery was victorious at the Battle of El Alamein?

E . . . . .

6   What is measured in dynes, newtons and poundals?

F . . . .

7   Actor who was labelled the 'King of Hollywood'.

G . . . .

8   Type of moustache with upward-curling ends.

H . . . .

9   Wild goat with high curved horns.

I . . .

10   Queen of the Netherlands 1948–1980.

J . . . . . .

11   Who wrote *The Water Babies* and *Westward Ho!*?

K . . . .

12   Of where is Monrovia the capital?

L . . . . . .

13   Chinese dynasty of 14th–17th century.

M . . .

14   Indian statesman whose byname was 'Pandit'.

N . . . .

15   The SI unit of electrical resistance.

O . .

16   Surname of Bonnie, of Bonnie and
Clyde fame.   P . . . . .

17   Soft, wet sand into which objects are
likely to sink.   Q . . . .

18   In golf, the Cup which is competed for
every two years between teams from USA
and Europe.   R . . . .

19   Chapel painted by Michelangelo from
1508 to 1512.   S . . . . . .

20   Who was the famous character
created by Edgar Rice Burroughs?   T . . . . .

21   Elliot Ness was the hero of the TV
series 'The ——'?   U . . . . ?

22   The US equivalent of the British music
hall.   V . . . .

23   Large, bowl-shaped metal pan used in
Chinese cooking.   W . .

24   A veil worn by Muslim women in
public.   Y . . . . . .

FOURTEEN

1 A vaulted recess.	A . . . . .
2 Bunch of flowers.	B . . . . . .
3 Deep fissure in a glacier.	C . . . .
4 Spanish gold coin.	D . . . .
5 Coffee-making machine.	E . . . .
6 Long legged scarlet bird.	F . . . .
7 Killing of giants.	G . . . .
8 Group of hounds.	H . . .
9 Tasteless.	I . . . . . .

10   A spirit able to assume human or
animal form.   J . . .

16

11	Inferior art or literature.	K . . . . .
12	One who polishes gems.	L . . . .
13	Perpendicular stroke at billiards.	M . . . .
14	Swimming.	N . . . . .
15	A bow or curtsey.	O . . . .
16	Currency of Chile.	P . . .
17	A pardoner.	Q . . . . . .
18	In which sport is the scissor shuffle?	R . . . .
19	Temperate grasslands of Europe.	S . . . . . .
20	Group of people.	T . . . . .
21	Uncombed.	U . . . . . .
22	Pertaining to a viper.	V . . . .
23	Byname of snooker's Jimmy White.	W . . . .
24	To cry out.	Y . . . . .

FIFTEEN

1	A motorway in a German-speaking country.	A . . . .
2	World champion darts player known as 'The Crafty Cockney'.	B . . . . . .
3	What is the game of draughts known as in USA?	C . . . .
4	Nickname of American jazz trumpeter John Birks Gillespie.	D . . . .
5	What word goes before eel, field and ray?	E . . . .
6	British coin, withdrawn from circulation in 1960.	F . . . .
7	Swedish film star born Greta Louisa Gustafsson.	G . . . .

8   Provincial capital of the Canadian state of Nova Scotia.   H......

9   The political scandal of 1986 which involved the Reagan Administration and Colonel Oliver North.   I.......

10   A young kangaroo.   J...

11   The sacred book of Islam.   K....

12   She appeared in the 'Road' films with Hope and Crosby.   L.....

13   Who said 'All I know is that I am not a Marxist'?   M...

14   In legend, who rode a sea-horse called a hippocampus?   N......

15   What does an oleometer determine the density of?   O..

16   George C. Scott won an Oscar for his portrayal of which American general in the 1970 film of the same name?   P.....

17   Rear section of the upper deck of a ship, usually reserved for officers.   Q..........

18   Mammal, such as a rat or squirrel, with incisor teeth used for gnawing.   R.....

19   Element with atomic no . 47 and symbol AG.   S.....

20   Opera composed by Puccini in 1900.   T....

21   Kung-fu and karate are examples of what type of combat?   U......

22   Of where is Caracas the capital?   V........

23   Name adopted by the British Royal Family in June 1917.   W......

24   The interest paid on a stock, share or bond.   Y....

1	A small fish.	A . . . . . .
2	Alloy of copper and tin.	B . . . . .
3	Stiff fabric petticoat.	C . . . .
4	Currency of Vietnam.	D . . .
5	Mouth of a river.	E . . . . . .
6	Portuguese melancholic song.	F . . .
7	Red in heraldry.	G . . . .
8	Group of gnats.	H . . . .
9	Triangle having two sides equal.	I . . . .
10	Military rulers of a country.	J . . . .
11	Brown Alaskan bear.	K . . . . .
12	Rope for securing horses.	L . . . . .
13	Study of minute objects.	M . . . .
14	Snow above the glacier.	N . . .
15	Blunt or rounded, not pointed or acute.	O . . . . .
16	Hungarian spice.	P . . . . . .
17	Mary——. British fashion designer.	Q . . . .
18	A rope ladder.	R . . . . . .
19	Mythological river of the underworld.	S . . .
20	Study of children.	T . . . .
21	An indefinitely large number.	U . . . . . .
22	A spiral.	V . . . . .
23	Australian war club.	W . . . .
24	French infantry soldier.	Z . . . . .

SEVENTEEN

1	In Islam, the God and supreme being of the Muslim faith.	A . . . .

2   City divided by the River Danube.   B . . . .

3   Who was the eldest son of Adam and Eve?   C . . .

4   Unit of length equal to 10cm.   D . . . .

5   Which TV soap features a fictional place called Hotton?   E . . . .

6   What word comes before lights, stories and tale?   F . . . .

7   Which region of Scotland was formed from the former counties of Aberdeen, Banff, Kincardine and most of Moray?   G . . . .

8   A person who gains unauthorised access to a computer system.   H . . . . .

9   In Greek mythology, the Goddess of the Rainbow.   I . . .

10   Horizontal beam supporting a ceiling.   J . . . .

11   Who served as US Secretary of State under Presidents Nixon and Ford?   K . . . .

12   Into what state do Just Souls go, which are barred from heaven through not being baptised?   L . . . .

13   What female Christian name means 'Wished-for child'?   M . . .

14   American gangster known as 'Baby Face'.   N . . . . .

15   The last letter of the Greek alphabet.   O . . . .

16   Of what are mafalde, conchiglie, macaroni and vermicelli types?   P . . . .

17   Any four-sided figure.   Q . . . .

18   Who was the first King of Rome?   R . . . . . .

19   Which event in American football takes place each January?   S . . . .

20

20 Girl's name which is also an anagram
of a Shakespeare play.   T . . . . .

21 Not requested or invited.   U . . . .

22 Active volcano in Campania,
Southern Italy.   V . . . .

23 The scandal which brought down
President Nixon.   W . . . .

24 To Westerners, what is Hatha the
most common form of?   Y . . .

EIGHTEEN

1	To walk about.	A . . . .
2	American tree of light wood.	B . . . .
3	Open-air game on a lawn.	C . . . . . .
4	Currency of Tunisia.	D . . . .
5	Flightless bird.	E . .
6	German harpsichord.	F . . . . .
7	Lively French dance.	G . . . .
8	Group of curlew.	H . . .
9	What do sailors call growlers?	I . . . .
10	Aromatic evergreen tree.	J . . . . . .
11	A small hill.	K . . . .
12	The vocal organ.	L . . . . .
13	Wine from Sicily.	M . . . . . .
14	Strong ale of E . Anglia.	N . .
15	Of the eyes.	O . . . . .
16	Study of soils.	P . . . .
17	Essence of a thing.	Q . . . .
18	Insignia of Royalty.	R . . . . . .
19	Japanese commander-in-chief.	S . . . . .

20	Group of magpies.	T . . . . .
21	Implement.	U . . . . . .
22	Patron saint of dancers.	V . . . .
23	A thin batter cake.	W . . . . .
24	Exclamation of anger.	Z . . . . .

NINETEEN

1	Who said 'Eureka! I've got it!'?	A . . . .
2	What type of ape lives on the Rock of Gibraltar?	B . . . . . .
3	What county of England was formed in 1974 from parts of Durham and Yorkshire?	C . . . .
4	What do Americans call curtains?	D . . . . .
5	By what name was Eva Perón otherwise known?	E . . . .
6	What number is 'fresh wind' on the Beaufort Scale?	F . . .
7	What word comes before headed, paced and up?	G . . . .
8	Who was the partner of British-born Arthur Stanley Jefferson?	H . . . .
9	In the Bible, the son of Abraham and Sarah and father of Esau and Jacob.	I . . . .
10	Form of dancing originating in the 1930s with the development of boogie-woogie.	J . . . .
11	In theatrical terms, what type of gore is imitation blood?	K . . . .
12	What are stalactites and stalagmites formed from?	L . . .
13	Who was the Poet Laureate from 1930 to 1968?	M . . . .

14	City in England famous for its lace.	N . . . .
15	The Japanese art of paper folding.	O . . . . . .
16	Who was Karol Josef Wojtyla known as from 1978?	P . . .
17	A province of Canada.	Q . . . . .
18	Who sculpted 'The Thinker'?	R . . . .
19	Who demanded John the Baptist's head on a plate?	S . . . . .
20	Unit of weight equal to 1000kg.	T . . . .
21	What is the best known book of the Irish writer James Joyce?	U . . . . . .
22	Any space in which no matter is present.	V . . . . .
23	Which film star's nickname was 'Duke'?	W . . . .
24	Which people are organised politically into the modern Inkatha movement?	Z . . .

TWENTY

1	Sun-dried brick.	A . . . .
2	Coloured silk handkerchief.	B . . . .
3	What is buckram?	C . . . .
4	Long Turkish robe.	D . . . . .
5	A heron.	E . . . .
6	Spanish dance.	F . . . .
7	Of where is Nuuk the capital?	G . . . .
8	Group of crows.	H . . . .
9	Body of African native fighters.	I . . .
10	Roman Catholic religious order.	J . . . . .
11	Poisonous snake.	K . . . .

12	Weariness.	L........
13	26-mile athletic's race.	M.......
14	What can be complex or real?	N......
15	The grunt of a pig.	O...
16	Study of disease.	P........
17	One who thinks he knows.	Q.......
18	Penguin's abode.	R......
19	Currency of Somalia.	S.......
20	Surveyor's instrument.	T.........
21	Two small islands of the Outer Hebrides.	U...
22	Carrion eating bird.	V......
23	A rug made from corn sacks.	W....
24	Skull-cap of R.C. ecclesiastic.	Z.......

TWENTY-ONE

1	What are the words 'post' and 'stop'?	A.......
2	What was the former name of the Hoover Dam?	B......
3	What game was invented by Mr Anthony Pratt of Birmingham in 1943?	C.....
4	What is the state capital of Australia's Northern Territory?	D.....
5	What is the name of the twelfth day after Christmas?	E.......
6	Decorative horizontal band, as along the top of a wall.	F.....
7	What well-known flower is a pelargonium a type of?	G.......
8	Measure equal to 4 inches of a horse's height.	H...

9   What league was formally established in 1956 to oversee inter-collegiate sports between prestigious colleges in USA?   I . .

10   What word comes before action, stock and tenant?   J . . . .

11   Who was the American food manufacturer whose company, founded in 1906, introduced cornflakes?   K . . . . . .

12   Type of mine which clings to a ship's hull by magnetic means.   L . . . . .

13   In which ship did the Pilgrim Fathers sail?   M . . . .

14   Gas used in illuminated signs.   N . . .

15   Furred, web-footed aquatic mammal.   O . . . .

16   The winged horse of Greek mythology.   P . . . . . .

17   A note equal in duration to half a crotchet.   Q . . . . .

18   What is hypegiaphobia the fear of?   R . . . .

19   Crazy Horse, who defeated Custer at the Battle of Little Big Horn (1876), was chief of which Indian tribe?   S . . . .

20   What do Americans call a dinner jacket?   T . . . . .

21   The bear in astronomy.   U . . .

22   The capital of Malta.   V . . . .

23   The Archbishop of Canterbury's special envoy, held hostage from 1987 to 1991.   W . . . .

24   North American river which was a major transportation route during the Klondike gold rush.   Y . . . .

1	Exercises to music.	A.......
2	Scots magistrate.	B......
3	Currency of Costa Rica.	C....
4	Group of snakes.	D..
5	Ox-like antelope.	E....
6	Killing of cats.	F.......
7	Sliding musical scale.	G........
8	One of the islands of Japan.	H.....
9	Living under an assumed name.	I........
10	Veins in the neck.	J......
11	One of the martial arts.	K.....
12	The will to live.	L.....
13	The egg-case of the dogfish.	M....../.....
14	Nuclear weapon.	N...
15	Small trip hammer.	O.....
16	What are buttered breadcrumbs on a menu?	P........
17	Not moving.	Q........
18	Card game derived from mahjong.	R....
19	Black in heraldry.	S....
20	What is a love apple?	T.....
21	Mountainous region of Italy.	U.....
22	Place where Teutonic heroes go to.	V.......
23	A sleeping-car.	W..../...
24	Gypsy.	Z......

| 1 | The Latin word meaning 'water-bearer'. | A....... |

2   Who scored 334 for Australia in the
Headingly Test of 1930?   B . . . . . .

3   Who said 'All I need to make a comedy
is a park, a policeman, and a pretty girl'?   C . . . . . .

4   What were Diplodocus, Coelophysis and
Stegosaurus?   D . . . .

5   What is meant by the prefix 'geo—'?   E . . . .

6   What do Americans call a tap?   F . . . . .

7   The famous address by Lincoln on 19th
November 1863 was on the site of which
battle?   G . . . .

8   Series of films, the first of which starred
Jamie Lee Curtis and Donald Pleasence in
1978.   H . . . .

9   A strip of land between water
connecting two much larger pieces of land.   I . . . . . .

10   What female Christian name is the
Cornish form of Guinevere?   J . . . .

11   Who wrote the *Jungle Books* and *Just
So Stories*?   K . . . . . .

12   Robert Banks Jenkinson was
otherwise known as the British Tory prime
minister the Earl of ——.   L . . . .

13   Where was the Russian revolutionary
Trotsky assassinated?   M . . . . .

14   Who called England 'a nation of
shopkeepers'?   N . . . .

15   Familiar group of stars representing a
hunter with belt and sword.   O . . . .

16   Glasgow-born US detective who in
1850 founded his national detective
agency.   P . . . .

17   What movement was founded by George Fox (1624–1691)?   Q . . . . . .

18   What is the North American caribou a type of?   R . . . .

19   What is the homophone for sale?   S . . .

20   What workman would use a spar hook, reed knife, shearing hook and eaves knife?   T . . . .

21   British playwright, author, actor and director, of Russian parentage.   U . . . . . .

22   1958 Alfred Hitchcock film which starred James Stewart and Kim Novak.   V . . . . . .

23   What substance is 'softened' by replacing calcium and magnesium ions with sodium and potassium?   W . . . .

24   Country, formerly Northern Rhodesia.   Z . . . . . .

TWENTY-FOUR

1   A voluntary sworn affirmation.   A . . . .

2   British colony in the NW Atlantic.   B . . . . . .

3   What is a Glengarry?   C . .

4   Australian wild dog.   D . . . .

5   Group of foxes.   E . . . .

6   Currency of Hungary.   F . . . . .

7   Reputed aphrodisiac.   G . . . . . .

8   Who painted 'The Laughing Cavalier'?   H . . .

9   Badge of office.   I . . . .

10   Tree with berry-like fruit.   J . . . . .

11   Silky fibre.   K . . . .

12   Outdoor swimming-pool.   L . . .

13 One of the French possessions in the
Caribbean.   M . . . .

14 State of perplexity.   N . . . . . .

15 Creature that eats any kind of food.   O . . . .

16 Who rescued Andromeda?   P . . . . . .

17 A final discharge.   Q . . . . . .

18 What does a potamologist study?   R . . . . .

19 Where does catgut come from?   S . . . .

20 Shape of a pediment.   T . . . .

21 Seventh planet from the Sun.   U . . . . .

22 Swing to and fro.   V . . . .

23 Small kangaroo.   W . . . . . .

24 Plant of the aster family.   Z . . . . .

TWENTY-FIVE

1 Sweet liqueur made of raw egg yolks
and brandy.   A . . . .

2 Art historian who admitted to spying
for the Soviet Union with Donald McClean
and Guy Burgess.   B . . . .

3 What was the nickname of the US
frontierswoman Martha Jane Burke?   C . . . .

4 What is measured by an odometer?   D . . . .

5 Technique of which Rembrandt was
the greatest master.   E . . . . . .

6 Whose own epitaph was 'On the whole,
I'd rather be in Philadelphia'?   F . . . . .

7 Country bounded by Côte d'Ivoire,
Burkina Faso and Togo.   G . . . .

8 He ran America's Federal Bureau of
Investigation for half a century.   H . . . . .

9 The scientific study of fishes. I . . . .

10 Pseudonym of British detective story writer Phyllis Dorothy White. J . . . .

11 Which fruit is also called Chinese gooseberry? K . . .

12 Who disappeared after the murder of his children's nanny Sandra Rivett? L . . . .

13 The Weaver and Irwell are tributaries of which river? M . . . . .

14 British actor, who in 1958 won an Oscar for his role in *Separate Tables*. N . . . .

15 A plane figure of eight sides and angles. O . . . . . .

16 Book or film which deals with events earlier than the previous work. P . . . . . .

17 Of where is Brisbane the capital? Q . . . .

18 A senior member of the Girl Guides. R . . . . .

19 What are phillips, crosshead and pozidrive? S . . . . .

20 What is triskaidekaphobia fear of? T . . . .

21 Republic in south east Europe, capital Kiev. U . . . . . .

22 Which name in Slavic means faith? V . . .

23 Which writer died in exile in Paris, having adopted the name of Sebastian Melmoth? W . . . .

24 The largest US National Park. Y . . . .

TWENTY-SIX

1 Slow pace in music. A . . . . .

2 Group of bishops. B . . . .

3	Small crown worn by a peer.	C . . . . . .
4	A large dog.	D . . . .
5	Fifth Greek letter of the alphabet.	E . . . . . .
6	Another name for a bassoon.	F . . . . . .
7	Home town of Christopher Colombus.	G . . . .
8	What is a hinny?	H . . . .
9	Study of ideas.	I . . . .
10	Wide-bodied airliner.	J . . . .
11	Japanese costume for women.	K . . . . .
12	Soil of sand and clay.	L . . .
13	Artist's colour.	M . . . . .
14	Public official.	N . . . . .
15	Excrement.	O . . . . .
16	What 'day' is Shrove Tuesday?	P . . . . . .
17	What male name means fifth-born?	Q . . . . . .
18	Glass chemical vessel.	R . . . . .
19	Currency of Peru.	S . .
20	Coarse outer garment.	T . . . . .
21	One-horned.	U . . . .
22	Who designed Castle Howard in Yorkshire?	V . . . .
23	French-speaking Belgian person.	W . . . . . .
24	A buffoon.	Z . . .

TWENTY-SEVEN

---

1   A ring of coral islands enclosing a lagoon.   A . . . .

2   Who was the British admiral after whom the inn in the novel *Treasure Island* was named?   B . . . . .

3   Member of cat family found on the American continent and otherwise known as puma, mountain lion, catamount and panther.   C . . . . .

4   Who, in the film *All about Eve*, said 'Fasten your seatbelts, it's going to be a bumpy night'?   D . . . .

5   Fourth largest of North America's Great Lakes.   E . . .

6   What is the capital of Sierra Leone?   F . . . .

7   Traditional Hungarian-style stew.   G . . . . . .

8   Beth, waw, mem and shim are all names of letters in which alphabet?   H . . . . .

9   What language is also known as Erse?   I . . . .

10   Who, in Roman mythology, was the wife of Jupiter?   J . . .

11   What was the professional surname of Daniel Kominski?   K . . .

12   In which institution is the Lutine Bell?   L . . . . .

13   What did Thomas Moule publish in the 19th century?   M . . .

14   In 1945–1946 it was the scene of German war criminal trials.   N . . . .

15   Ground which is headquarters of Surrey County Cricket Club.   O . . .

16   In Greek mythology, who opened the box releasing all the evils into the world?   P . . . . . .

17   A fruit related to the pear.   Q . . . . .

18   The title of a king as used in lawsuits.   R . .

19   In which prison was Rudolf Hess imprisoned until his death in 1987?   S . . . . . .

20   The name of Neptune's three-pronged spear.   T . . . . . .

21	The last syllable of a word.	U . . . . .
22	In Roman mythology, who was the Goddess of victory?	V . . . .
23	What is the name of the 'Concerto' that the British composer Richard Addinsell composed for the film *Dangerous Moonlight* (1941)?	W . . . . .
24	Metal frame to assist walking by elderly or infirm persons.	Z . . . . .

TWENTY-EIGHT

1	The frigate bird.	A . . . .
2	Large Indian rat.	B . . . .
3	Casino dice game.	C . . . .
4	Pertaining to a duke.	D . . . .
5	Group of oarsmen.	E . . . .
6	Study of animal distribution.	F . . . .
7	Music hall of the lowest class.	G . . .
8	What is *Apis millifera*?	H . . . .
9	Upper part of the hip-bone.	I . . . .
10	What male forename means in Hebrew, 'one who takes by the heel'?	J . . . .
11	The hartebeest.	K . . . .
12	A Scots lake.	L . . .
13	Type of baboon.	M . . . . . , . .
14	Central part of a church.	N . . .
15	Wet mud.	O . . .
16	Zoroaster lived where?	P . . . . .
17	Variety of scallop.	Q . . .
18	Attaches itself to sharks .	R . . . . .
19	Group of musicians.	S . . . . .

20	Hot capsicum sauce.	T . . . . . .
21	English legendary saint.	U . . . . .
22	Snake.	V . . . .
23	Spoil sport.	W . . . . .
24	Style of bookbinding.	Y . . .

TWENTY-NINE

1	The largest snake in the world.	A . . . .
2	When Lenin seized power in Russia by what name were the revolutionary Marxist socialists known?	B . . . .
3	Who wrote *Lord Jim* and *Under Western Eyes*?	C . . . . .
4	Another name for the thermos flask, after its inventor.	D . . . .
5	What were developed by James Watt in 1765 and Otto Diesel in 1892?	E . . . . . .
6	Sport which takes place on a piste.	F . . . . . .
7	Angel who is recorded in the Bible as fortelling the births of John the Baptist and Jesus.	G . . . . . .
8	Australian Prime Minister succeeded in 1991 by Paul Keating.	H . . . .
9	Which town was the birthplace of Cardinal Wolsey and home of Thomas Gainsborough?	I . . . . . .
10	Who is the patron saint of carpenters?	J . . . . .
11	The capital of Afghanistan.	K . . . .
12	Who said 'The ballot is stronger than the bullet'?	L . . . . . .
13	Apart from English, which is the other official language of New Zealand?	M . . . .

34

14 What does the letter 'N' of the abbreviation 'E.N.T.' stand for? N . . .

15 The smallest of the five Great Lakes. O . . . . . .

16 Musical term meaning very fast. P . . . . .

17 A savoury pastry shell. Q . . . . .

18 Famous creation of John Mortimer. R . . . . . .

19 What are Pitmanscript, Gregg and Teeline types of? S . . . .

20 A term used for a bird-watcher. T . . . .

21 Unplanned, without forethought. U . . . .

22 The wife of a Viceroy. V . . . .

23 Leather band used to fasten the neck squares of a Scout or Guide. W . . . . .

24 Country formerly Southern Rhodesia. Z . . . .

THIRTY

1 Original name for Ethiopia. A . . . .

2 Flat round cake of barley meal. B . . . . . .

3 West Indian folk song. C . . . . . .

4 A gold coin. D . . . .

5 European coin. E . .

6 The right to vote. F . . . .

7 Old fellow. G . . . . .

8 Another name for daddy-longlegs. H . . . .

9 Put to death with sharp stake. I . . . . .

10 Lace frill worn at the neck. J . . . .

11 New Zealand parrot. K . . .

12 Shiny. L . . . . .

13 Served with cheese sauce. M . . . . .

14 Study of the kidneys. N . . . .

15	Express an opinion.	O . . . .
16	3.25 light years.	P . . . . .
17	A fully-developed female bee.	Q . . . .
18	Neck band with flaps.	R . . . .
19	Oysters rockefeller served on bed of?	S . . . . . .
20	Implied but not impressed.	T . . . .
21	The quality or state of being everywhere.	U . . . .
22	System of magic in West Indies.	V . . . . .
23	Carpet shark.	W . . . .
24	Of a yellowish colour.	X . . . . . .

THIRTY-ONE

1	Small country in the Pyrenees.	A . . . . . .
2	Which model village was established in 1879 by the brothers George and Richard Cadbury for their workers?	B . . . .
3	In the 19th century Astley's and Spangler's was one.	C . . . . .
4	Aboriginal wind instrument with long wooden tube.	D . . . .
5	Who wrote the oratorio *The Dream of Gerontius?*	E . . . .
6	What have flat blades called vanes and side branches called barbs?	F . . . .
7	Who did Harold Wilson succeed as leader of the Labour Party on his death in 1963?	G . . . .
8	Which country had a police force called the tonton-macoutes?	H . . . .
9	What can be both fluid and crystallised?	I . . . .

10   In which month each year do the Isle of Man TT races take place?

J . . .

11   Where are Frankfort, Louisville and Lexington?

K . . . .

12   What is a beaver's den called?

L . . . .

13   William Lamb was otherwise known as the British Whig Prime Minister Viscount ——.

M . . . .

14   The home town of Jesus for most of his life.

N . . . .

15   Independent sultanate in the Arabian peninsula.

O . . .

16   Norman Mailer (1980), John Updike (1982) and Anne Tyler (1989) were winners of which literary prize?

P . . . .

17   Who was the hunchbacked character in Victor Hugo's novel of 1831 *Notre Dame de Paris*?

Q . . . .

18   Enormous bird of Arabian legend.

R . .

19   What do Americans call the card game of patience?

S . . . .

20   What kind of plays are *Hamlet*, *Othello*, *King Lear* and *Macbeth*?

T . . . .

21   Moneylender who charges an exorbitant rate.

U . . . . .

22   A wine-merchant.

V . . . . . .

23   A golf club with very wide-angled face.

W . . . .

24   Which stadium in New York is affectionately known as 'The house Babe Ruth built'?

Y . . . . .

1	Hindu nurse for children.	A . . .
2	Small cake soaked in rum.	B . . .
3	Disease of the eye.	C . . . .
4	Man-made fibre of acrylic.	D . . . . .
5	A sandal.	E . . . .
6	Curved like a sickle.	F . . . . . .
7	Senile.	G . . .
8	One who frequents a place.	H . . . . . .
9	An island.	I . . .
10	Money pool at card games.	J . . . . . .
11	Malayan fox-bat.	K . . . . .
12	Game played with counters.	L . . .
13	Vocal composition in harmony.	M . . . .
14	Amenhotep's wife.	N . . . .
15	Species of willow.	O . . . .
16	Who were '*les fouvres*' in France?	P . . . .
17	Wager on first and second.	Q . . . .
18	Dog hunted by scent.	R . . . .
19	Currency of Israel.	S . . . . .
20	Habitually silent.	T . . . .
21	Dark yellow-brown pigment.	U . . . .
22	Greedy in eating.	V . . . .
23	Rodent poison.	W . . . .
24	Wooden tissue.	X . . . .

THIRTY-THREE

1   The first man to set foot on the moon was Neil Armstrong . Who was his companion on that flight and second man to set foot on the moon?   A . . . . .

2   In physics, whose law states that at a constant temperature the volume of a gas varies inversely with its pressure?   B . . . . .

3   What did Mary Tudor say would be found lying in her heart when she was dead and opened?   C . . . . .

4   Book compiled in 1086 on the orders of William The Conqueror.   D . . . .

5   Who, in Greek mythology, was punished by Hera so that she could only repeat another speaker's last words?   E . . .

6   Who directed such films as *Amarcord* and *La Dolce Vita*?   F . . . . . .

7   What is the name of the hammer used by chairpersons at meetings?   G . . . .

8   Laser-produced 3D photograph or pattern.   H . . . .

9   Where, in 1964 and 1976, were the Winter Olympic Games held?   I . . . .

10   Seventh President of US, nicknamed 'Old Hickory'.   J . . . . . .

11   What is the base SI unit of mass?   K . . . .

12   What was relieved by General Buller in the Boer War in February 1900?   L . . . .

13   State capital of Wisconsin USA.   M . . . . . .

14   Clouds which produce rain or snow.   N . . . . .

15   An official who investigates complaints regarding administrative action by governments.   O.........

16   What is a hedonomaniac addicted to?   P.......

17   The enforced isolation of persons exposed to contagious disease.   Q.........

18   Type of music popularised by Scott Joplin.   R......

19   Who said 'Let us drink to the queer old dean'?   S......

20   In Russia, what would be contained in a 'samovar'?   T..

21   Smoothly polite and refined.   U.....

22   A type of hot Indian curry.   V.......

23   Who said that in future everyone would be famous for fifteen minutes?   W.....

24   A young upwardly-mobile professional.   Y.....

THIRTY-FOUR

1	Deep blue of the sky.	A....
2	Tropical bird similar to toucan.	B.....
3	Spanish gentleman.	C........
4	Elderly female companion.	D.....
5	Coloured unbleached linen.	E...
6	Portable folding tent.	F........
7	Horse's hock.	G......
8	Japanese verse of seventeen syllables.	H....
9	Sleeplessness.	I.......
10	Thigh-length boot.	J.......
11	Currency of Iceland.	K....

12	Good or bad person.	L...
13	Child's card game.	M......
14	Pale red colour.	N......
15	Folded together.	O.......
16	Star-shaped.	P........
17	Country house.	Q.....
18	Madagascan palm.	R.....
19	Group of mares.	S...
20	Large variety of extinct hound.	T.....
21	Fleshy organ hanging from back of throat.	U....
22	Readily evaporating.	V.......
23	Traveller.	W.......
24	Instrument for scraping bones.	X.....

THIRTY-FIVE

1	What would you find in a formicary?	A...
2	Which showman said 'There's a sucker born every minute'?	B.....
3	Who was the eponymous hero of a 1759 Voltaire novel?	C......
4	Writer of *The Count of Monte Christo* and *The Three Musketeers*.	D....
5	The point on the surface of the earth above the focus of an earthquake.	E........
6	Argentinian motor-racing driver, World Champion five times 1951, 1954–1957.	F.....
7	Where in the Lake District is Dove Cottage, the home of Wordsworth?	G.......
8	Who painted *A Rake's Progress*?	H......

9   An economic situation where the general level of prices is rising.   I . . . .

10   Style of English early Renaissance architecture.   J . . . .

11   The name of which famous diamond means in Hindu 'mountain of light'?   K . . . .

12   The land of tiny people in *Gulliver's Travels*.   L . . . .

13   The patron saint of accountants, book-keepers and tax collectors.   M . . . . . .

14   What is the capital of Cyprus?   N . . . . . .

15   Turkish dynasty of 14th–20th century.   O . . . . . .

16   How would you describe someone unduly fussy about details?   P . . . .

17   A small game bird.   Q . . . .

18   Democratic device also known as a plebiscite.   R . . . .

19   What are lazy-daisy, vandyke and holbein?   S . . . .

20   What is Formosa now called?   T . . . . .

21   Act of 1662 prescribing the form of public prayers in the Church of England.   U . . . .

22   French film director who married Brigitte Bardot.   V . . . .

23   Who said that the Battle of Waterloo was won on the playing fields of Eton?   W . . . .

24   The sixth letter of the Greek alphabet.   Z . . .

THIRTY-SIX

---

1   The sign &.   A . . . .

2   A rich soup.   B . . . . .

3   Savoury ball of meat and potato.   C . . . .
4   Musical instrument with strings.   D . . . .
5   Currency of Cape Verde Islands.   E . . . . .
6   Chinese gambling game.   F . . / . . .
7   A guard.   G . . . .
8   Large shed for aircraft.   H . . . . .
9   Rolled up.   I . . . .
10   A male ass.   J . . . . . .
11   What in Ghana is the 'City of the
Golden Stool'?   K . . . . .
12   Of a lake.   L . . . . .
13   Dish of mixed vegetables.   M . . . .
14   Streamlined body housing engine on
plane.   N . . . . . .
15   Diagonal rib or vault.   O . . . .
16   Son-in-law of Julius Caesar.   P . . . . .
17   Traitor.   Q . . . .
18   Branching.   R . . . . .
19   The chief alloy of iron.   S . . . .
20   Long cloak.   T . . . .
21   To furnish with cushions.   U . . . .
22   Fashion prevalent at a certain time.   V . . . .
23   State of matrimony.   W . . . . . .
24   Currency of China.   Y . . .

THIRTY-SEVEN

1   What is measured by the SI unit
radian?   A . . . . .
2   Who composed the musicals *On the
Town* and *West Side Story*?   B . . . .

3   Who wrote *The Rime of the Ancient Mariner*?

C . . . .

4   Type of fruit cake with almonds.

D . . . . .

5   Muslim prince or head of state.

E . . .

6   Japan's highest peak.

F . . . .

7   What is the Hellenic Republic?

G . . . . .

8   Who scored 364 runs for England against Australia at the Oval in 1938?

H . . . . .

9   A document specifying details of an offence of which a person is accused.

I . . . .

10   British politician who co-founded the Social Democratic Party in 1981.

J . . . . . .

11   Species of bird of the kingfisher family which has a loud laughing cry.

K . . . .

12   1952 film in which Charles Chaplin starred, directed and composed the music.

L . . . .

13   Which mountain in Alaska is the highest elevation on the North American continent?

M . . . .

14   What was patented in America in 1937 by Wallace H . Carothers?

N . . . .

15   Who was the American athlete who embarrassed the Nazis by winning four gold medals at the 1936 Olympics?

O . . . .

16   The familiar pattern of seven bright stars within Ursa Major.

P . . . . .

17   A quarter section of a circle.

Q . . . .

18   Whose ride from Charleston to Lexington was immortalised in a poem by Longfellow?

R . . . . .

19   Australian term for a tramp, vagrant or itinerant worker.

S . . . . . .

20 Mexican town whose name is associated with musician Herb Alpert.   T . . . . . .

21 What something is if it is *sui generis*?   U . . . . .

22 What are retinol, thiamine and pyridoxine?   V . . . .

23 Known to his friends as 'Plum', who created the characters Jeeves and Wooster?   W . . . .

24 Residential suburb on the River Hudson to the north of New York.   Y . . . . . .

THIRTY-EIGHT

1	Thieves' slang.	A . . . .
2	Roman galley with two banks.	B . . . . .
3	Mare's tail clouds.	C . . . . .
4	Coarse cloth like calico.	D . . . .
5	An eagle.	E . . .
6	Magazine for fans of a celebrity.	F . . . . . .
7	Spanish nobleman.	G . . . . . .
8	A game played on 256 squares.	H . . . .
9	To make black.	I . . . .
10	Fast light car.	J . . .
11	Currency of Denmark.	K . . . .
12	Eleventh letter of Greek alphabet.	L . . . . .
13	Fine leather from goat.	M . . . . . .
14	Crisp corn chip from Mexico.	N . . . .
15	Study of the car.	O . . . . . .
16	Name given to the five regular solids.	P . . . .
17	Curl lying flat on the forehead.	Q . . . .
18	Embankment.	R . . . . . .
19	Group of hounds.	S . . . . .

20	South American tick.	T . . . . .
21	Cloven-hoofed animal.	U . . . .
22	A kind of typeface.	V . . . .
23	The sky.	W . . . . .
24	To chatter.	Y . . . . .

THIRTY-NINE

1	Where is the seaport of Anchorage?	A . . . . .
2	What is the main ingredient of stroganoff?	B . . .
3	Tennis player who was known as 'Little Mo'.	C . . . .
4	The removal of salt from sea-water.	D . . . .
5	From where did Napoleon escape on 20th March 1815?	E . . .
6	Historic region of Europe famous for woven tapestry.	F . . . .
7	The fruit of the thorny shrub *ribes grossularia*.	G . . . .
8	Who became Poet Laureate in 1984?	H . . . . .
9	In the 11th century, which people established their capital at Cuzco, the sacred city of the Sun?	I . . . .
10	An impure variety of quartz.	J . . . . .
11	What was partitioned along the 38th parallel in 1945 after Japan's defeat?	K . . . .
12	What is 'the forbidden city'?	L . . . .
13	In which TV series did Bruce Willis and Cybill Shepherd star as partners in a private detective agency?	M . . . .
14	On what river does the port of Buffalo stand?	N . . . . . .

15 What is indicated by the prefix 'dis'?   O . . . .

16 Who, in 1936, composed *Peter and the Wolf*?   P . . . .

17 The prickly spine of a porcupine or hedgehog.   Q . . . .

18 The capital of Saudi Arabia.   R . . . . .

19 In which city were the Archduke Franz Ferdinand and his wife assassinated by a Bosnian student in June 1914?   S . . . .

20 What is a wheatear a type of?   T . . . . .

21 What female Christian name means 'little she-bear'?   U . . . . .

22 Of what is lexicology the study?   V . . . .

23 Which inventor first used the term horse-power?   W . . .

24 Who became President of Russia in 1991?   Y . . . . . .

FORTY

1	Greek Goddess of Love.	A . . . .
2	Mantle or cloak worn by Arab.	B . . . . . .
3	Buttocks of a horse.	C . . . .
4	Quilt stuffed with down.	D . . . .
5	A sea urchin.	E . . . . . .
6	Gambling game at cards.	F . . .
7	Killing a race of people.	G . . . .
8	Type of rope.	H . . . . .
9	The letter Z.	I . . . . .
10	Wicked bold woman.	J . . . . . .
11	Tenth letter of Greek alphabet.	K . . . .
12	Rustic French bagpipe.	L . . . .

47

13	Aggressive assertiveness.	M . . . .
14	The head.	N . . .
15	No good (slang).	O . . . .
16	Another name for a block.	P . . . . .
17	Large stone.	Q . . . .
18	Edge or margin.	R . . .
19	Group of trees.	S . . . . . .
20	Swine-like mammal.	T . . . .
21	Mythical animal with horn.	U . . . . . .
22	The use of many words without necessity.	V . . . .
23	Breed of long-haired sheep.	W . . . .
24	West Indian tree.	Y . . . .

FORTY-ONE

---

1 Fred Astaire started in Vaudeville as a double-act with his sister in 1916. What was her name?   A . . . .

2 Who was the French minstrel said to have found Richard I in an Austrian prison in 1193?   B . . . . . .

3 In cricket, an off-break bowled by a left-handed bowler to a right-handed batsman.   C . . . .

4 Which name is derived from Dionysus, the Greek God of Wine?   D . . . . .

5 Lancashire town which gives its name to a type of cake.   E . . . . .

6 The last King of Egypt (1937–1952).   F . . . . .

7 What was the name of Elvis Presley's home in Memphis?   G . . . .

8   The Astros (baseball), Rockets (basketball) and Oilers (football) are major league teams of which US city?   H . . . . . .

9   What, in Hindi, is called Bharat?   I . . . .

10   A type of artichoke.   J . . . .

11   British Field Marshal and War Secretary who was drowned in the North Sea in 1916.   K . . . .

12   Dublin stands at the mouth of which river?   L . . . . .

13   Whose mistress was Claretta Petacci?   M . . . .

14   Of what is rhinology the study?   N . . . .

15   In Shakespeare's *A Midsummer Night's Dream* who was King of the Fairies?   O . . . . .

16   The only golfer to win a major tournament in each of four decades.   P . . . . .

17   Of where is Doha the capital?   Q . . . .

18   Whose byname was 'FDR'?   R . . . .

19   A famous one took place in Sydney Street in 1910.   S . . . .

20   What island group was previously called The Friendly Isles?   T . . . .

21   Deep blue pigment formerly obtained from lapis lazuli.   U . . . .

22   The point at which two lines meet to form an angle.   V . . . . .

23   Blue dye used as skin covering by Ancient Britons.   W . . .

24   Outer, coloured skin of citrus fruits.   Z . . .

FORTY-TWO

1   Square-hewn stone.   A . . . . .

2	Smooth flattering speech.	B . . . . . .
3	Group of stars.	C . . . . . .
4	Arabian camel.	D . . . .
5	Learned.	E . . . . . .
6	Confused mixture.	F . . . . . .
7	Davis Straits separates Canada from.	G . . . .
8	Mohammed's flight from Mecca.	H . . . . .
9	Set of facial features on transparencies.	I . . . .
10	Medieval entertainer.	J . . . .
11	Kind of wooden hammock.	K . . . . .
12	Currency of Sierra Leone.	L . . . .
13	Heavy woollen blankets.	M . . . .
14	American cactus.	N . . . .
15	Rare Atlantic fish.	O . . .
16	Roman God Neptune, name of Greek God?	P . . . .
17	Proportional share.	Q . . . .
18	A rejection.	R . . . . .
19	Group of foxes.	S . . . .
20	Light two-wheeled cart.	T . . . .
21	Hoof, claw or talon.	U . . . . .
22	Forbidden by authority.	V . . . .
23	Small white-rumped bird.	W . . . .
24	Small opossum.	Y . . . .

FORTY-THREE

1	What type of a plant is a Michaelmas Daisy?	A . . . .
2	To what does the adjective volucrine refer?	B . . . .

3   The study of codes and ciphers.   C . . . .

4   What are timbals, tabors and tablas?   D . . . .

5   What Christian name in Norse originally meant 'ruler of all'?   E . . .

6   Who created Captain Horatio Hornblower?   F . . . .

7   Who was the first American to orbit the Earth in space?   G . . . .

8   She starred with Henry Fonda in the film *On Golden Pond* and with Humphry Bogart in *The African Queen*.   H . . . . . .

9   Which British novelist, author of *Goodbye to Berlin*, inspired the musical *Cabaret*?   I . . . .

10   What comes before miller, public and soap?   J . .

11   Tralee is the administrative centre of which Irish county?   K . . . .

12   Another name for tetanus.   L . . . . . .

13   Footballer who played right-wing for England and was known as the 'wizard of the dribble'.   M . . . .

14   Who was the father of Japheth, Ham and Shem who are depicted as the ancestors of all the nations on earth?   N . . .

15   Common name of the African bird *Struthio camelus*.   O . . . . . .

16   What type of numbers are 2, 3, 5, 7, 11, 13 and 17?   P . . . .

17   A common colourless crystalline mineral.   Q . . . . .

18   Whose best known work was the *Thesaurus of English Words and Phrases* (1852)?   R . . . .

51

19 What is the name of the whole note O? S . . . .

20 What is the name of the square in China where major demonstrations, and subsequent massacre, took place in 1989? T . . . .

21 The official language of Pakistan. U . . .

22 A knight's page in former times. V . . . . .

23 Who invented the bouncing bomb of Dambusters fame? W . . . . .

24 Set of tuned wooden bars struck with small hard hammers. X . . . .

FORTY-FOUR

1 Cloud known as mackerel sky. A . . . / . . . .

2 American song bird. B . . . .

3 Kind of pumpkin. C . . . .

4 Training of horses in deportment. D . . . .

5 Bolt for french windows. E . . . .

6 Litter of pigs. F . . . . .

7 Wine from Bordeaux. G . . . . .

8 Study of the sun. H . . . .

9 Commenced. I . . . .

10 In dance, a jump from one foot to another. J . . .

11 Deep ravine. K . . .

12 Currency of Honduras. L . . . . . .

13 Small sponge cake. M . . . .

14 Australian plant. N . . . . .

15 Medium-sweet golden sherry. O . . . . . .

16 Confection of almond and sugar. P . . . . . .

17 Artful trick. Q . . . .

18 Temperature of a gas oven. R . . . . .

19	Group of teal.	S . . . . .
20	Chinese secret society.	T . . .
21	A pitcher or urn-shaped organ.	U . . . .
22	Roman goddess of the hearth.	V . . . .
23	A light shallow rowing boat.	W . . . . .
24	Style of bookbinding.	Y . . .

FORTY-FIVE

| 1 | The African ant-eater. | A . . . . |

2   Who crossed Niagara Falls on a tightrope in 1859?   B . . . . . .

3   In the film *White Heat* his famous last words were 'Look, Ma! Top of the world!'   C . . . . .

4   What do Americans call a nappy?   D . . . . .

5   The code name given to the German armed forces ciphers in World War II.   E . . . . .

6   What is the meaning of the African word 'Boer'?   F . . . . .

7   *Rainbow Warrior*, sunk by French agents in Auckland Harbour in July 1985, was the vessel of which organisation?   G . . . .

8   What is trichology the study of?   H . . .

9   A line on a weather map joining places of equal temperature.   I . . . .

10   What are torque, ouch, girandole and labret types of?   J . . . .

11   Composer of the musical *Showboat*.   K . . .

12   In the abbreviation PLR what does the letter 'L' stand for?   L . . . . . .

13   Nyasaland is the former name of which African republic?   M . . . . .

14 Who lost the 1960 US election to John F. Kennedy? N . . . .

15 Who solved the riddle of the Sphinx? O . . . . . .

16 Playwright whose works include *The Birthday Party* (1958) and *The Caretaker* (1960). P . . . . .

17 Assess or ascertain the amount of. Q . . . .

18 Of what was Smith and Wesson a famous make? R . . . .

19 Apart from the sun, which is the brightest star visible in the night sky? S . . . . .

20 Home of the O'Hara family in *Gone With the Wind*. T . . .

21 The twentieth letter in the Greek alphabet. U . . . . . .

22 A dance in slow waltz time. V . . . . .

23 Australian furry burrowing marsupial. W . . . . .

24 Mystical form of Buddhism. Z . .

FORTY-SIX

1 Sweet red wine from Spain. A . . . .

2 Inventor of steel producing system. B . . . .

3 What does a nephoscope measure? C . . . . .

4 Sweetmeats of nuts and fruit. D . . . . .

5 Level space for walking. E . . . .

6 An easy armchair. F . . . .

7 Gem associated with January. G . . . . .

8 Hannibal's father. H . . . .

9 Studio slang for incandescent lights. I . . . . .

10 Religion of the Jews. J . . . . . .

11	What is American for paraffin?	K . . . .
12	Name the second Pope.	L . . . .
13	To celebrate an event uproariously.	M . . . . . .
14	Lowest tide.	N . . .
15	Mountain nymph.	O . . . .
16	Relating to dinner.	P . . . .
17	Spoke.	Q . . . .
18	Morning signal to awaken troops.	R . . . .
19	Group of herons.	S . . . .
20	Killing of bulls.	T . . . .
21	Central American black bear.	U . . . .
22	The ancient Hebrew scriptures.	V . . .
23	Watery part of milk after curds separated.	W . . .
24	Safe-breaker.	Y . . .

FORTY-SEVEN

1	A word having the opposite meaning to another.	A . . . . . .
2	Who was released from the cross instead of Jesus?	B . . . .
3	Who wrote *Uncle Vanya*?	C . . . . . .
4	Small writing desk with side drawers.	D . . . .
5	Oedipus complex in a young girl.	E . . . . . .
6	In America it is a transom, what is it called in England?	F . . . .
7	Who wrote the words to *Trial by Jury*?	G . . . . . .
8	Out of which city did the Pied Piper charm the rats?	H . . . . . .

9   Who, in 1948, designed the Morris Minor and, in 1959, the Mini?   I . . . .

10   Small measure for alcoholic drinks.   J . . . . .

11   The Hindu God of Love.   K . . .

12   The palace of the archbishop of Canterbury.   L . . . . . .

13   Who, on leaving the Philippines in 1942, said 'I shall return'?   M . . . .

14   What type of bomb is an 'enhanced radiation weapon'?   N . . . . . .

15   Joan Plowright is the widow of which British actor?   O . . . . . .

16   What are salmon called during the first two years of their life?   P . . .

17   The result of dividing one quantity by another.   Q . . . .

18   Villain played by Frank Gorshin in the 1966 *Batman* movie.   R . . . . . .

19   A place where illicit liquor was sold during the American Prohibition era.   S . . . .

20   Who wrote *The Charge of the Light Brigade*?   T . . . .

21   Where would you find San José, Fray Bentos and Salto?   U . . . . . .

22   Short decorative curtain hung along a pelmet.   V . . . . . .

23   Another name for a gnu.   W . . . .

24   Plucked string instrument.   Z . . . . .

FORTY-EIGHT

1   The state of baldness.   A . . . .

2   Inventor of carpet sweeper.   B . . . . . .

3	Of table and chair legs.	C.......
4	Eastern guide.	D.......
5	South American cattle estate.	E.......
6	Ukulele in Hawaiian meant originally.	F...
7	Another name for chickpea.	G.......
8	Type of furniture.	H..........
9	Son of Daedalus.	I.....
10	Roman emperor called the 'Apostate'.	J.....
11	A bundle.	K....
12	Type of chicken.	L......
13	Fern with delicate fronds.	M...../....
14	A headland.	N...
15	Supplication.	O.....
16	Crustacean.	P....
17	Plinth of a podium.	Q.....
18	Light entertainment with song.	R....
19	Group of bitterns.	S....
20	Rolling top of a writing desk.	T......
21	Of the navel.	U........
22	Mouse-like rodent.	V...
23	Buttermilk.	W...
24	East Indian measure of distance.	Y....

FORTY-NINE

---

1 A score at golf of three under par at one hole.   A........

2 Who wrote *The Threepenny Opera?*   B.....

3 Word coined from the ministry of Clifford, Arlington, Buckingham, Ashley and Lauderdale in the reign of Charles II?   C....

4 Character played by Stanley Holloway in *My Fair Lady*.

D . . . .

5 The philosophy of morals and moral choices.

E . . . . .

6 What is meant by the mathematical symbol '!'?

F . . . .

7 Fabled creature said to be the offspring of the lion and the eagle.

G . . . . . .

8 What company was founded by Sir Terence Conran?

H . . . . . .

9 To collapse inwards.

I . . . . . .

10 American golfer who won the Grand Slam in 1930.

J . . . .

11 Where in America did Orville and Wilbur Wright make the first flight by a heavier-than-air machine?

K . . . .

12 The capital of Angola.

L . . . . .

13 What is meant by the prefix 'poly–'?

M . . .

14 A smooth-skinned variety of peach.

N . . . .

15 British athlete who won the 800 metres title in the 1980 Olympics.

O . . . .

16 Which Russian word means truth?

P . . . . .

17 The national airline of Australia.

Q . . . . . .

18 Archibald Philip Primrose was otherwise known as the British Liberal Prime Minister, the Earl of ——.

R . . . .

19 The only man to win both the World Motor-cycle and World Motor-racing Championships.

S . . . . . .

20 Who had a sign on his desk 'the buck stops here'?

T . . . . .

21 The study of ultrasound.

U . . . .

22 Short pointed beard after the style of a 17th-century Flemish painter. V . . . . . .

23 Former name of Sellafield, the nuclear power plant in Cumbria. W . . . .

24 Where did the conference take place in February 1945 between Churchill, Stalin and Roosevelt? Y . . . .

FIFTY

1 Secretion from the cachalot whale. A . . . .

2 Shoulder belt for cartridges. B . . . .

3 Another name for aquilegia. C . . . .

4 Study of the skin. D . . . .

5 Characteristic spirit. E . . . .

6 Estate held under feudal tenure. F . . .

7 Museum in New York. G . . . .

8 Oriental porter. H . . . . .

9 Soaring too high. I . . . . . .

10 A scarecrow. J . . . / . . . . .

11 Two-masted Dutch fishing vessel. K . . .

12 Hybrid between hare and rabbit. L . . . .

13 Indian corn. M . . . .

14 Refrain in old ballads. N . . . .

15 Left over. O . . .

16 A mandate. P . . . . . .

17 Wager on four winners. Q . . . .

18 Oblique parallelogram. R . . . .

19 Ancient trombone. S . . . . . .

20 Currency of Bangladesh. T . . .

21 Umbrella-shaped appendage. U . . . .

22	Intuition.	V . . . .
23	Breed of racing dog.	W . . . . . .
24	Rare metallic element.	Y . . . . . .

1	The US term for a lawyer.	A . . . .
2	Republic on the Gulf of Guinea, West Africa.	B . . . .
3	Flying Fish Cove is the capital of which Australian island in the Indian Ocean?	C . . . .
4	American baseball player with New York Yankees who married Marilyn Monroe in 1952.	D . . . .
5	What was the name of Captain Cook's ship?	E . . . .
6	What is meant by the prefix 'tetra–'?	F . . .
7	The name of sixteen Popes, the last being in 1846.	G . . . . . .
8	From where does the ukulele originate?	H . . . . .
9	A Spanish or Portuguese princess other than the heir apparent.	I . . . . . .
10	Swiss psychiatrist associated with Sigmund Freud.	J . . .
11	What is a kindle a group of?	K . . . . . .
12	In horse racing, at which French racecourse is the Prix de l'Arc de Triomphe held annually?	L . . . .
13	What was the byname of the British Labour politician Emmanuel Shinwell?	M . . . .

14 English Civil War battle in which the
Royalist forces under Charles I were
defeated by Parliament's 'New Model'
Army under Fairfax.   N . . . . .

15 If Orient is West, what is East?   O . . . .

16 What is parian ware, crackle ware
and nankeen?   P . . . .

17 The theory that energy transferences
occur in bursts of a minimum quantity.   Q . . . . . .

18 Nickname of William II, King of
England 1087–1100.   R . . . .

19 In the James Bond stories, of which
criminal organisation is Ernst Stavro
Blofeld the head?   S . . . . . .

20 Of what are transitional, sans-serif
and contempory examples?   T . . . .

21 Mountain range in Russia.   U . . . .

22 Covered with a sticky substance.   V . . . . .

23 What does a wainwright build or
repair?   W . . . . .

24 The longest river in China.   Y . . . . . .

FIFTY-TWO

1	Helps a priest at mass.	A . . . . . .
2	Shoulder belt for a sword.	B . . . . . .
3	Light Welsh boat.	C . . . . . .
4	Regular solid with twelve faces.	D . . . .
5	Thin slices of meat.	E . . . .
6	Indentation in a brick.	F . . .
7	Russian guitar.	G . . . .
8	Oriental bath house.	H . . . . .

61

9	One who manages a concert.	I.........
10	A novice.	J.......
11	A fruit.	K......
12	Opium prepared in alcohol.	L.......
13	Shapeless piece.	M......
14	Mountain peak projecting through ice sheet.	N......
15	One of the Italian people.	O....
16	An abstract.	P.....
17	One who brags of his medicine.	Q..........
18	Foundation of loose stones.	R.....
19	Group of bears.	S.....
20	French kettle-drum.	T......
21	African bird.	U.......
22	A freebooter.	V.....
23	A gadget.	W.....
24	Chinese tree.	Y....

FIFTY-THREE

1	Name of the desert in Chile.	A......
2	Western TV series that featured the Cartwright family.	B......
3	18th-century Italian writer of erotic memoirs.	C.......
4	What is the name of the hourglass-shaped toy that is thrown and caught on a cord held between the hands?	D......
5	Portuguese footballer whose byname was 'the Black Pearl'.	E......

6   The youngest daughter of the prophet
Mohammed.   F . . . . .

7   What is meant by the musical term
'grazioso'?   G . . . .

8   What was designed by Christopher
Cockerell in 1950?   H . . . .

9   What is iconology the study of?   I . . . . .

10   What male Christian name means
bringer of treasure?   J . . . . .

11   Shrimp-like, small marine creatures.   K . . . .

12   Who was the lyricist who wrote the
score of *Gigi* in 1958?   L . . . . .

13   The official language of Hungary.   M . . . . .

14   Who was the youth in Greek
mythology who fell in love with his
reflection in a pool?   N . . . .

15   Who wrote the opera *The Tales of
Hoffmann*?   O . . . .

16   Who, in 1660, wrote *And so to bed*?   P . . . .

17   Size of book in which sheets are folded
into four leaves.   Q . . . . .

18   A pickled herring fillet, sometimes
wrapped round an onion.   R . . . . . .

19   What type of front does this symbol
signify in meteorology ？   S . . . .

20   The art of shaping plants.   T . . . . . .

21   French painter famous for his street
scenes of Paris, particularly Montmartre.   U . . . . . .

22   An entrance hall or lobby.   V . . . .

23   American merchant who started a
chain of five-and-ten-cent stores
throughout the USA?   W . . . .

63

24 Brothers who were part of the Jesse James outlaw gang.   Y . . . . . .

1	The egg plant.	A . . . .
2	Currency of Thailand.	B . . .
3	Range of columns.	C . . . .
4	Odd-numbered pages.	D . . . . .
5	Animal with no incisors.	E . . . .
6	Shallow depression.	F . . . .
7	Fear of women.	G . . . .
8	Hirsute.	H . . . .
9	Small bone in the middle ear.	I . . . .
10	A huntsman.	J . . . . .
11	A narrow channel.	K . . .
12	Decked with laurel.	L . . . .
13	Sea cow.	M . . . . . .
14	Brandy cordial with flavour of bitter almonds.	N . . . . .
15	Killing of sheep.	O . . . . . .
16	Biscuit of wheaten flour.	P . . . . . .
17	Cleft into four parts.	Q . . . .
18	Group of knaves.	R . . . . .
19	Small loose-skinned orange.	S . . . . . .
20	Bull-like.	T . . . . . .
21	Having woolly or curly hair.	U . . . .
22	Culture of grape vines.	V . . . .
23	North American sandpiper.	W . . . . .
24	Not giving milk.	Y . . .

FIFTY-FIVE

1   Former KGB chief who was USSR leader
in 1982–1984.   A . . . .

2   Who was the mother of politician
Shirley Williams, whose writings include
Testament of Youth?   B . . . .

3   What are Lepus, Hercules and Draco?   C . . . .

4   A squirrel's nest.   D . . .

5   The instant when the Sun lies directly
overhead at the Equator.   E . . . . . .

6   What do Americans call a leave of
absence from military duty.   F . . . .

7   What type of book is a Baedeker?   G . . . .

8   Who was Lyndon Baines Johnson's
vice-president from 1965–1969?   H . . . .

9   In geology what sort of rock is produced
by volcanic action?   I . . . . . .

10   What is the best-known work of the
British composer Sir Hubert Parry?   J . . . .

11   A desert in Africa.   K . . . .

12   Which showman said 'I cried all the
way to the bank'?   L . . . .

13   What is 'spondulix' slang for?   M . . . .

14   Which country was formerly
South-West Africa?   N . . . . . .

15   The second husband of Jacqueline Lee
Bouvier.   O . . . . . .

16   What did Clyde Tombaugh discover
on 18th March 1930?   P . . . .

17   Inflammation of throat or tonsils.   Q . . . . .

18   A match of three games in bridge or
whist.   R . . . . .

19 Who was the wicked hypnotist of George du Maurier's novel *Trilby*? S . . . .

20 Of where in South Africa is Pretoria the state capital? T . . . .

21 Type of bread eaten by Jews during the Passover. U . . . .

22 Relating to the spring. V . . . . .

23 The long-running soap *Coronation Street* is set in which fictional district? W . . . .

24 The fifth of the noble gases recovered from the atmosphere. X . . . .

FIFTY-SIX

1   Defence made of fallen tres. A . . . . .
2   Group of rooks. B . . . .
3   Tapioca is made from this root. C . . . . . .
4   A whirling religious mendicant. D . . . . . .
5   Study of the environment. E . . . . . .
6   Kind of sweetmeat. F . . . . . .
7   Shin armour. G . . . . . .
8   A Scottish dish of liver and oatmeal. H . . . . .
9   Naïve girl. I . . . . . .
10 A louvre blind. J . . . .
11 Asian wild ass. K . . . .
12 Bank of river formed by silt. L . . . .
13 Jaw. M . . . .
14 Shining, bright. N . . . .
15 End-blown ivory horn. O . . . .
16 Lesser Dog Star. P . . . . . .
17 Magistrate having charge of public funds. Q . . . .

18	Type of face powder.	R . . . . .
19	Group of princes.	S . . . .
20	Set of four elements.	T . . . . . .
21	Growing in swampy plains.	U . . . .
22	She-fox.	V . . . .
23	Separate chaff from grain.	W . . . . .
24	Twentieth letter of the Greek alphabet.	Y . . . . . .

1	Airline of Russia, code name SU.	A . . . .
2	During which battle did the Charge of the Light Brigade take place?	B . . . .
3	Who was the plumber by appointment to King Edward VII who invented the flushing lavatory?	C . . . . . .
4	What male Christian name means 'dark water'?	D . . . . . .
5	What did the Polish physician Lazarus Ludwig Zamenhof invent?	E . . . .
6	An imperial unit equal to nine gallons.	F . . . . .
7	Cricketing position between third-slip and point.	G . . . .
8	Dissident Czech author, jailed for nine months in 1989 but who became President of Czechoslovakia later that same year.	H . . . .
9	The Muslim religion.	I . . . .
10	What large vehicular word means in Sanskrit 'protector of the world'?	J . . . .
11	The capital of Uganda.	K . . . . . .
12	Third book of the Old Testament.	L . . . .

13 Who was the British aviator who, in 1932, married Amy Johnson?   M.......

14 The Japanese name for Japan.   N.....

15 A figure with eight faces.   O.........

16 What would you find in a book called a missal?   P......

17 A portable case for arrows.   Q.....

18 What is the capital of Morocco?   R....

19 The furthest point north or south of the Equator that the Sun reaches each year.   S.......

20 American writer who created the character Pudd'nhead Wilson in his 1894 detective story.   T....

21 To seize or take possession of without right.   U....

22 Church service in the late afternoon or evening.   V......

23 American swimmer and film star who portrayed Tarzan in 19 films.   W..........

24 What is a hank a bundle or measure of?   Y...

FIFTY-EIGHT

1 The white poplar.   A....

2 Wooden-headed golf club.   B....

3 Shell-like curve.   C.......

4 Central tower or keep in castle.   D.....

5 Slow plaintive song.   E....

6 Pocket handkerchief.   F....

7 Group of mallard.   G....

8	A fence sunk between slopes.	H . . .
9	Figure cut on a hard surface.	I . . . .
10	Ornamental pot.	J . . . .
11	Water spirit.	K . . . . .
12	Reading desk.	L . . . . . .
13	Type of roof.	M . . . . . .
14	A hobgoblin.	N . .
15	Study of birds.	O . . . .
16	Currency of Botswana.	P . . .
17	North American tree.	Q . . . .
18	Radar beacon.	R . . . .
19	Group of jellyfish.	S . . . .
20	Currency of Mongolia.	T . . . . .
21	Cavalryman with a lance.	U . . . .
22	Autonomous region of E. Spain.	V . . . .
23	One pretending to learning.	W . . . .
24	Yellow-hammer.	Y . . . . .

FIFTY-NINE

1	What are trefoil, ogee, lancet and parabolic types of?	A . . . . .
2	What is the name of Japan's high-speed train?	B . . . . .
3	Home of the Duke of Devonshire.	C . . . .
4	British judge, Master of the Rolls (1962–82) and author of the book *The Road to Justice* (1955).	D . . . . . .
5	What does the letter 'E' stand for in the abbreviation L.E .D.?	E . . . .

6 What do miners call methane occurring in coal mines?   F.......

7 Another name for the eucalyptus tree.   G..

8 What name in Greek originally meant 'bright shining one'?   H....

9 What are silverfish, springtail and psocids?   I......

10 What word comes before bear, fowl and juice?   J.....

11 Standing on the Arabian Sea, it is Pakistan's principal seaport.   K......

12 Whose book, *The Spirit of St Louis*, won the Pulitzer Prize in 1954?   L........

13 The code name used by the US for the project from 1942 which developed the atomic bomb.   M........

14 A shout of joy in Christmas carols.   N....

15 Name for a person born or living in the Orkneys.   O.......

16 During World War I, what were Rupert Brooke and Wilfred Owen?   P....

17 Unusually bright, star-like object outside our galaxy with large red-shifts.   Q.....

18 West Indian type of rock jazz with a two-beat rhythm.   R.....

19 A five-pointed echinoderm.   S.......

20 Bookmakers' system of hand signals at racecourses.   T.......

21 The 'ology' concerned with the study of unidentified flying objects.   U......

22 What was the name of the USSR space mission which achieved the first manned orbital flight in April 1961?   V.....

23 What shape is described as 'cuneal' or 'sphenic'?   W....

24 Where in Virginia did British forces under Cornwallis surrender in 1781?   Y.......

1	Currency of Afghanistan.	A......
2	Italian drinking song.	B.......
3	Bell ringing.	C..........
4	Sweet soft music.	D....
5	Sea holly.	E.....
6	Strip of land kept clear of trees.	F........
7	Organ stop with nasal horn.	G.......
8	Wind that blows from the Sudan.	H....:.
9	Situated within the ribs.	I..........
10	Study of newspapers.	J.........
11	Double full cheese.	K......
12	A basket.	L....
13	Release from slavery.	M......
14	Writing frame for the blind.	N.........
15	Group of hermits.	O.........
16	Six-sided prism.	P..............
17	Four-leaved.	Q...........
18	Flint instrument for scraping.	R......
19	An old experienced person.	S.....
20	Hindu spot on forehead.	T....
21	Freehold tenure.	U...
22	Rotating spiral of fluid.	V.....
23	A Maori woman.	W.....

24 Where are Shibam, Ta'izz, Tarim and
Hodeida?   Y....

SIXTY-ONE

1 Use of words starting with the same
letter or sound, for example, 'big black box'. A...........

2 What is vespertilian an adjective for?   B..

3 What colour is produced by the primary
colours of blue and green?   C...

4 Which suffragette threw herself under
the King's horse in the 1913 Derby?   D.......

5 What was the name of the spacecraft
which on 20th July 1969 landed the first
man to walk on the Moon?   E....

6 19th-century US engineer who
designed the giant fairground wheel.   F.....

7 Which Russian word, which in the
1980s became known as the new Soviet
philosophy of thinking aloud, means
'speaking aloud'?   G.......

8 The name of Sherlock Holmes' faithful
housekeeper.   H.....

9 Which female Christian name means
'beloved child'?   I.....

10 What is a Portuguese man-of-war a
type of?   J........

11 Another name for paraffin.   K.......

12 Which political cartoonist created
Colonel Blimp?   L..

13 King of Scotland who killed Macbeth.   M......

14 In the Bible, the fourth book of the
Penteteuch.   N......

15 Epic poem attributed to Homer describing the wanderings of Ulysses after the fall of Troy.

O . . . . . .

16 What type of numbers are 6, 28, 496 and 8128?

P . . . . . .

17 A piece of tobacco for chewing.

Q . . .

18 Who played the gangster Rico in the film *Little Caesar*?

R . . . .

19 White linen, knee-length garment worn by clergy.

S . . . .

20 Instrument used to record speeds and times of use of vehicles.

T . . . .

21 To scold or criticise sharply.

U . . . . . .

22 A finely calibrated scale named after a 17th-century French mathematician.

V . . . . . .

23 Who did Richmal Crompton write about?

W . . . . . .

24 Persian king defeated by the Greeks in the Persian Wars.

X . . . . .

SIXTY-TWO

1	Largest artery of the body.	A . . . .
2	Group of ferrets.	B . . . .
3	Currency of Ghana.	C . . .
4	With criminal intent.	D . . . . .
5	To blanch.	E . . . .
6	The fur of the polecat.	F . . . .
7	Currency of Haiti.	G . . . . .
8	Inventor of the pendulum clock.	H . . . . . .
9	Having regular flowers.	I . . . .
10	Young Australian sheep.	J . . . . . .

11	Elephant enclosure.	K . . . .
12	To thrash.	L . . . . .
13	Study of divination.	M . . . .
14	Large petrel.	N . . . .
15	Italian name for Piccolo.	O . . . .
16	Study of veins.	P . . . .
17	Common round clam.	Q . . . . . .
18	Explosive.	R . . . .
19	Group of subalterns.	S . . . .
20	Spanish ballad.	T . . . . .
21	Fruitfulness.	U . . . . .
22	God of Fire.	V . . . . .
23	New Zealand spirit.	W . . . . . .
24	River gum eucalyptus.	Y . . . . .

SIXTY-THREE

1 White marble-like stone.   A . . . .

2 Who was the President of Cuba overthrown in January 1959 prior to Fidel Castro coming to power?   B . . . . . .

3 Of which country is Yaounde the capital?   C . . . .

4 Who was the British aeronautical engineer whose company produced the Mosquito, Vampire and Comet aircraft?   D . . . .

5 US inventor of rolled film and the Kodak camera.   E . . . . . .

6 What is a blacksmith's hammer called?   F . . . . .

7 Which clarinettist and bandleader was known as the 'King of Swing'?   G . . . . . .

8 What is stygiophobia fear of?   H . . .

9 A pure gelatin found in fish.   I . . . .

10 Who would wear a coxcomb and
motley and carry a bauble?   J . . . . .

11 Production company of silent films
(1912–1919) founded by Mark Sennett.   K . . . .

12 What company was founded by Sir
John Moores in 1923?   L . . . .

13 Illicit whisky, especially in southern
US states.   M . . . .

14 Who wrote the song 'Keep the Home
Fires Burning'?   N . . . . . .

15 What is the main ingredient of the
dish angels-on-horseback?   O . . . . . .

16 Prison situated on the Isle of Wight. P . . . .

17 The pure and concentrated essence of
any substance.   Q . . . .

18 French revolutionary leader who
introduced the Reign of Terror and the cult
of the supreme being.   R . . . .

19 In which seaside resort did Billy Butlin
open his first holiday camp?   S . . . .

20 Who killed the Minotaur in the Cretan
labyrinth?   T . . . . . .

21 The quantity that a cask wants of
being full.   U . . . . .

22 If recto is odd-numbered pages of a
book, what are the left-hand
even-numbered pages called?   V . . . .

23 Which composer wrote the film music
for Olivier's films of *Henry V*, *Hamlet* and
Richard III?   W . . . . .

24 Pseudonym of the British novelist
Cecil William Mercer (1885–1960).   Y . . . .

1	Edible gasteropod mollusc.	A . . . . . .
2	Group of mules.	B . . . . .
3	18th-century stringed keyboard instrument.	C . . . .
4	Large aquatic mammal.	D . . . . .
5	Slightly raised platform.	E . . . . . .
6	Having the toes separated.	F . . . .
7	Oriental warehouse.	G . . . . .
8	Old English oboe.	H . . . . . .
9	Greyish yellow.	I . . . . .
10	Species of stork from South America.	J . . . . .
11	Tartar circular tent.	K . . . . . .
12	Sweetmeat with medicinal purposes.	L . . . .
13	Currency of Finland.	M . . . . .
14	Removal of a kidney.	N . . . .
15	Oblong gold coin.	O . . . .
16	Harsh scolding.	P . . . .
17	Bulb of a liliaceous plant.	Q . . . . . .
18	Block of hardwood to polish marble.	R . . . .
19	North Indian fiddle.	S . . . . . .
20	Achilles' mother.	T . . . . .
21	Superman.	U . . . .
22	Like a vulture.	V . . . .
23	French hunting horn.	W . . . .
24	Jolly-boat.	Y . . .

SIXTY-FIVE

1   St Anne's is the administrative centre

for which British island?   A . . . .

2   John, Lionel and Ethel were part of which famous acting family of the first half of the 20th century?   B . . . .

3   Airline of Ireland, code name CZ.   C . . . . .

4   Fine, delicate china made at Meissen in Germany since 1710.   D . . . . . .

5   Tree which produces edible fruit called persimmons.   E . . . .

6   Thirteenth President of the USA.   F . . . .

7   Who said 'I'll give you a definite maybe'?   G . . . . . .

8   Unit of liquid volume equal to 100 litres or 22 gallons.   H . . . .

9   The name of 13 Popes between 402 and 1724.   I . . . .

10   Who uses Indian clubs?   J . . . .

11   Energy associated with an object's motion.   K . . . . . .

12   Who was the beggar in Jesus' parable of the rich man and the poor man?   L . . . . . .

13   Country formerly known as Burma.   M . . . . . .

14   What was the maiden name and pen name of Mrs Hubert Bland, who wrote *The Railway Children*?   N . . . . .

15   A variety of quartz resembling agate.   O . . .

16   Sophy was the title of the King of which country in ancient times?   P . . . . .

17   Couch-grass.   Q . . . . .

18   Whose first film was *Love is on the Air* (1937)?   R . . . . .

19   What shape is described as 'ensform', 'gladiate' or 'xiphoid'?   S . . . .

20 Who, in medieval stories, is the lover of Cressida? T . . . . . .

21 Country and university city of East Sweden. U . . . . . .

22 The evening star Venus, appearing just after sunset, is given what name? V . . . . .

23 What is meant by the suffix '–latry'? W . . . . . .

24 Who succeeded Joseph Smith as President of the Morman Church in 1844? Y . . . .

SIXTY-SIX

1	Currency of Argentina.	A . . . . . .
2	Group of boys.	B . . . .
3	Type of sheep dog.	C . . . . .
4	Italian cathedral.	D . . . .
5	An apparition.	E . . . . . .
6	Long narrow inlet into the sea.	F . . . .
7	Study of old age.	G . . . .
8	Study of the liver.	H . . . .
9	Having teeth all alike.	I . . . . . .
10	Species of wading-bird.	J . . . . .
11	A little child.	K . . . . . .
12	A lake.	L . . . .
13	Fear of contamination.	M . . . .
14	Pertaining to small ships.	N . . . .
15	Small coin of Ancient Greece.	O . . .
16	Ancient British chief.	P . . . .
17	Small Australian tree.	Q . . . . . .
18	Currency of Cambodia.	R . . .
19	Another name for zinc.	S . . . . . .

20	Tarot pack of cards.	T . . . .
21	Museum in Florence.	U . . . . .
22	What unisex forename means lively?	V . . . . .
23	Tree of the rice family.	W . . . . .
24	Leaf fly.	Z . . . .

SIXTY-SEVEN

1	Where, in Virginia, is the Pentagon situated?	A . . . .
2	What was invented in 1839 by a West Point cadet Abner Doubleday?	B . . . .
3	What musical term means 'in a singing style'?	C . . . .
4	Another name for a foxglove or such related plant.	D . . . .
5	Which religion worshipped the Sun-god Re, the Sky-god Norus and the Moon-god Toth?	E . . . .
6	To what does the adjective sylvan refer?	F . . . . . .
7	The playing field in American football.	G . . . .
8	What is measured by a hygrometer?	H . . . .
9	What Russian word means 'news'?	I . . . .
10	What female Christian name means in Celtic 'champion' or 'lord'?	J . . . .
11	An Australian marsupial.	K . . . .
12	In Greek legend, who was the lover of Hero?	L . . . . . .
13	Who was the sister of Moses?	M . . . . .
14	The main prison of the City of London up to 1902.	N . . . . . .
15	What was the pseudonym of Eric Arthur Blair?	O . . . . .

16 Group of freelance photographers who badger celebrities. P........

17 The first Sunday in Lent. Q...........

18 What is the better-known name of Israel Beer Josephat (1816–99), the British founder of the first news agency? R.....

19 What are cantle, skirt, flap and pommel all parts of? S......

20 What was the name of the reed boat in which Thor Heyerdahl, in 1977/8, made a journey from Iraq to Djibouti? T.....

21 In Greek mythology, the Muse of Astronomy. U.....

22 An early form of cycle propelled by the feet. V.........

23 Who said 'Liberty, when it begins to take root, is a plant of rapid growth'? W.........

24 Who was the father of James and John, two of the twelve Apostles of Jesus? Z......

SIXTY-EIGHT

1	Ancient gun.	A........
2	Engraver's tool.	B....
3	Deep volcanic crater.	C......
4	Indian ruler's court.	D.....
5	The sweet briar.	E........
6	Smoked dried haddock.	F.....
7	Present name of Gold Coast.	G....
8	Fear of sleep.	H..........
9	Lack of will or testament.	I........
10	North Spanish dance in triple time.	J...

11	Currency of Burma.	K . . .
12	Pronged fishing spear.	L . . . . . .
13	Title of Japanese emperors until 1867.	M . . . . .
14	Dreamy musical piece.	N . . . .
15	Government body which monitors B.T.	O . . . .
16	Invader of Peru.	P . . . . . .
17	A jellyfish.	Q . . . .
18	Medieval three-stringed instrument.	R . . . .
19	On a menu, what is florentine?	S . . . . . .
20	Incense container.	T . . . .
21	Rump of a fowl.	U . . . .
22	Wrote a best-seller in prison.	V . . . .
23	Large white North American owl.	W . . . . . .
24	A stockade.	Z . . . . .

SIXTY-NINE

1 Who was the 19th-century British jockey who rode 2748 winners in his career and committed suicide at Newmarket? A . . . . .

2 Thimphu is the capital of which kingdom in the Himalayas? B . . . . .

3 What are long staple, medium staple and short staple types of? C . . . . .

4 1950's TV series starring Jack Webb. D . . . . . .

5 Which palace is the official residence of the French President? E . . . . .

6 Cave celebrated in Mendelssohn's Hebrides Overture. F . . . . . .

7 Who wrote *The Wind in the Willows*? G . . . . . .

8 Ancient Egyptian picture writing. H . . . .

9   Christian name of the American lyric writer who collaborated with his brother George Gershwin.   I . .

10   British painter, mainly of portraits, for example, of Lloyd George, George Bernard Shaw and T .E . Lawrence.   J . . . .

11   Densely populated peninsula and region of Hong Kong.   K . . . . . .

12   What street is synonymous with London's banking and financial world?   L . . . . . .

13   What colour is produced by the primary colours blue and red?   M . . . . . .

14   Which architect designed Marble Arch?   N . . .

15   Where, in Florida, is Walt Disney World?   O . . . . . .

16   Whose law states that 'Work expands so as to fill the time available for its completion'?   P . . . .

17   Slang term for a prison.   Q . . .

18   Which author created Billy Bunter?   R . . . .

19   Who wrote *Rosencrantz and Guildenstern are Dead*?   S . . . .

20   What is the capital of Albania?   T . . . . .

21   Hook-shaped.   U . . . .

22   A Venetian water-bus.   V . . . .

23   Who wrote *Brideshead Revisited*?   W . . . .

24   In Greek mythology, whose shield was the 'aegis'?   Z . . .

SEVENTY

1   Metal tip of a shoelace.   A . . . .

82

2	Lullaby for a baby.	B.......
3	Horseshoe-shaped basin.	C...
4	Malevolent West Indian ghost.	D....
5	Study of deserts.	E........
6	An informer.	F...
7	Flat round cake.	G......
8	Group of hares.	H...
9	A nickle steel alloy.	I....
10	South American wild cat.	J.........
11	Currency of Angola.	K.....
12	Irish folklore dwarfish sprite.	L.........
13	What is the kissing disease?	M............
14	SI unit of force.	N.....
15	A cry of lamentation.	O....
16	Practice.	P.....
17	A weight of 100 or 112 lbs.	Q......
18	Currency of Maldives.	R......
19	Cuttlebone comes from?	S....
20	Another word for boastful.	T..........
21	Study of astrology.	U........
22	Forceps with hooked teeth.	V.......
23	North American prairie dog.	W..........
24	To hit or smack.	Z..

SEVENTY-ONE

1 Character played by Leslie Howard in
the film *Gone With the Wind*.   A.....

2 What does a tegestologist collect?   B.......

3 Polo's Gold Cup is held annually at
which Park in Sussex?   C......

4   Name given to the reference guide to the titled aristocracy of Great Britain.   D . . . .

5   What type of poems are the Sumarian *Gilgamesh*, Homer's *Iliad*, the Indian *Mahabharata* and the English *Beowulf*?   E . . . .

6   Nocturnal beetle also known as glowworm and lightning bug.   F . . . . . .

7   Who was the French doctor who, in the 18th-century, invented a method of execution?   G . . . .

8   Gas used in fluorescent lighting tubes, lasers and balloons.   H . . . . .

9   What is meant by the mathematical sign ∞?   I . . . .

10   Glossy black lacquer or varnish.   J . . . .

11   Game reserve of South Africa named in honour of a former President.   K . . . . .

12   To what does the adjective lacustrine refer?   L . . . .

13   The brother of Sherlock Holmes.   M . . . . . .

14   Language that is deliberately distorted for propaganda purposes.   N . . . .

15   The art and practice of public speaking.   O . . . . . .

16   What shape is 'pyriform'?   P . . .

17   Form of religion with passive attitude to life.   Q . . . .

18   Therapeutic foot massage.   R . . . .

19   Whose shops' slogan was 'the customer is always right'?   S . . . .

20   What was the name of the first satellite which enabled live TV to be transmitted between Europe and America?   T . . . . . .

21	A rain-gauge.	U . . . .
22	A farewell speech.	V . . . .
23	Popular resort beach in Hawaii.	W . . . . . .
24	Fashionable Swiss skiing resort.	Z . . . . . .

SEVENTY-TWO

1	Irregularly shaped.	A . . . .
2	Bearing berries.	B . . . . . .
3	Three-headed dog of Hades.	C . . . .
4	Short clay tobacco pipe.	D . . . .
5	Negotiator.	E . . . .
6	Strike with the nail of the finger.	F . . . . .
7	Large ship with three or four decks.	G . . . . . .
8	Cross between two different strains.	H . . . . .
9	Angry.	I . . . . . .
10	Unit of radiation received from outer space.	J . . . . .
11	Fear of stooping.	K . . . .
12	Leather shorts with braces.	L . . . .
13	Romeo's surname.	M . . . .
14	Wise old man in Homer.	N . . . . .
15	A simpleton.	O . . . .
16	Consisting of land or farms.	P . . . . . .
17	South American tree.	Q . . . . . .
18	Of rhubarb.	R . . . .
19	Political crisis of 1956.	S . . .
20	Fear of the sea.	T . . . .
21	Type of narrow-winged moth.	U . . . .
22	Passing through the air.	V . . . . .

| 23 | Marmoset. | W . . . . . . |
| 24 | Short-horned buffalo. | Z . . . . . . |

---

1 Which science fiction writer wrote the *Foundation Trilogy*?	A . . . . .
2 Which Scottish author was Governor-General of Canada from 1935–1940?	B . . . . .
3 The site where Jesus was crucified.	C . . . . . .
4 US gangster known as 'Public Enemy Number One'.	D . . . .
5 What can be linear, quadratic or cubic?	E . . . .
6 Which Archbishop of Canterbury crowned Queen Elizabeth II?	F . . . . .
7 The largest known tortoise is native to which island group?	G . . . .
8 Who wrote *Tess of the d'Urbervilles*?	H . . . .
9 Farsi is the official language of which country?	I . . .
10 What are leyden and canopic types of?	J . . .
11 Thermometer scale in which zero is absolute zero.	K . . . . .
12 Adjective pertaining to the left side of a vessel.	L . . . .
13 What is musophobia fear of?	M . . .
14 A Jew in biblical times.	N . . . .
15 Bird of prey, otherwise known as fish hawk or fish eagle.	O . . . . .
16 Which American explorer was the first to reach the North Pole?	P . . . .
17 Occurring every fourth day.	Q . . . . . .

18　Dover, Sandwich, Hastings and Hythe were four of the five original Cinque Ports. Which was the fifth?　　R . . . . .

19　Who may use a gorget, a bistoury, a trephine or a speculum?　　S . . . . . .

20　Who wrote *The Secret Life of Walter Mitty*?　　T . . . . . .

21　Church or religious movement known as the 'Moonies'.　　U . . . .

22　An old-fashioned word for sulphuric acid.　　V . . . . . .

23　What would you find in a vespiary?　　W . . . .

24　Animal also known as Brahman cattle or humped cattle.　　Z . . .

SEVENTY-FOUR

1	Group of clergymen.	A . . . .
2	A small cask.	B . . . . . .
3	Study of whales.	C . . . .
4	Drizzling mist.	D . . .
5	The mouth of a river.	E . . . .
6	A freebooter.	F . . . .
7	Where is the River Essequibo?	G . . . . .
8	Calcutta is on which river?	H . . . . . .
9	Worship of Isis.	I . . . .
10	Island of the Inner Hebrides.	J . . .
11	Study of beauty.	K . . . .
12	Long heavy stick.	L . . . .
13	Dance from Africa.	M . . . . . .
14	Thick muslin.	N . . . .
15	Third stomach of a ruminant.	O . . . . .

16	Pert young fellow.	P . . . .
17	Another name for the hawthorn.	Q . . . .
18	Stock of musical pieces.	R . . . .
19	Study of the Moon.	S . . . .
20	Leader of first crusaders.	T . . . . . .
21	Type of fruit.	U . . .
22	Glass showcase.	V . . . . . .
23	Hobgoblin.	W . . . .
24	An hors d'oeuvre.	Z . . . . . .

SEVENTY-FIVE

1 Of what did John Ruskin write 'The chemistry of it is more like a medieval doctor's prescription than the making of a respectable mineral'?   A . . . .

2 The brother of Charlotte, Emily and Anne Brontë.   B . . . .

3 Reference Point (1987) and Slip Anchor (1985) were horse-racing's Derby winners ridden by which jockey?   C . . . . . .

4 Cooking term meaning to coat with flour or sugar.   D . . . . .

5 The capital of a company belonging to the shareholders.   E . . . . .

6 A person who shoes horses.   F . . . . . .

7 Of where is Libreville the capital?   G . . . .

8 What shape is described as 'cornual'?   H . . .

9 What is the better-known name of the US dancer Angela Duncan (1877–1927)?   I . : . . . .

10 Calendar established in 46BC and used in Europe until 1582.   J . . . . .

88

11 A common agricultural settlement in Israel. K ......

12 Followers of the 14th-century English reformer John Wycliffe. L ....

13 Persecution of suspected Communist sympathisers in the US in the 1950s. M ....

14 Who was the Goddess of Vengeance in Greek mythology. N ......

15 The island-region of the Pacific and adjoining seas. O ......

16 What is Lutetia the ancient name of? P ....

17 A stanza of four lines. Q ....

18 Another name for German measles. R ......

19 A salaried and legally qualified magistrate. S ....

20 Who wrote *Barchester Towers* and *Phineas Finn*? T ....

21 A period of time allowed for payment of a foreign bill of exchange. U .....

22 An overbearing, scolding woman. V ....

23 A species of which bird is called pipits? W ......

24 Czechoslovak runner whose four Olympic titles included the 5,000 metres, 10,000 metres and marathon in the 1952 Games. Z ......

SEVENTY-SIX

1 Cashew nut. A .....

2 A small camel. B ....

3 Old American dance. C ....

4 Fleshy fruit with a stone. D ....

5	Chapel or meeting place.	E.......
6	Pertaining to a son or daughter.	F.....
7	Loose breeches.	G...........
8	Another name for underground.	H.......
9	Moving from place to place.	I........
10	Birth story of Buddha.	J.....
11	Fear of dust.	K.........
12	Killing hares.	L.........
13	Phnom Penh is on which river?	M.....
14	Venomous snake similar to cobra.	N...
15	Derived from oil.	O....
16	Long narrow Malayan canoe.	P...
17	Ball of savoury paste.	Q.......
18	Cowardly.	R......
19	Study of the flesh.	S......
20	Scholar of Queens College, Oxford.	T.......
21	To disentangle.	U......
22	A small rod.	V......
23	A shaft sunk from one level to another.	W....
24	Dessert of egg yolk.	Z.........

SEVENTY-SEVEN

1	F. Murray Abraham won an Oscar for his performance in which film of 1984?	A......
2	An archaic word for sulphur.	B........
3	Resort island in Brooklyn named from the Dutch word for rabbit.	C....
4	What was the name of the Roman practice of killing every tenth man in a	

cowardly or mutinous military unit? D . . . .

5 Of where is Tallinn the capital? E . . . . . .

6 Château used by Napoleon as his
Imperial Palace. F. . . . .

7 What word refers to heat from the
Earth's interior used as an energy source? G . . . .

8 What is a spinet a small type of? H . . . .

9 Who wrote *Hedda Gabler*? I . . . .

10 In Greek legend, the mother of
Oedipus. J . . . . . .

11 Town which gives its name to a type
of carpet made there. K. . . . .

12 Mayor of New York from 1933–1945
who gave his name to one of that city's
airports. L . . . .

13 In music, what is meant by the term
'con sordino'? M . . . .

14 The post supporting the handrail at
either end of a flight of stairs. N . . . .

15 Opera is the plural of which word? O . . .

16 The nearest point to the Earth during
the Moon's orbit. P . . . . . .

17 A system of recording and
reproducing sound using four speakers. Q . . . .

18 Who was the music hall comedian
dubbed the 'prime minister of mirth'? R . . . .

19 Which theatre in London first staged
the operas of Gilbert and Sullivan? S . . . .

20 A 300th anniversary. T . . . .

21 A blue or black clay lying close to a
vein of coal. U . . .

22 Another name for chicken-pox. V . . . .

23 What are the zonda, the khamein, the
bise and the harmattan? W . . . .

24 Fear of strangers or foreigners. X . . . .

SEVENTY-EIGHT

1	Having two sharp edges.	A . . . .
2	Group of conies.	B . . .
3	Invader of Mexico.	C . . . . .
4	Oatmeal and water uncooked.	D . . . .
5	Short pastoral poem.	E . . . . . .
6	Pertaining to a thread.	F . . . .
7	West Indian lizard.	G . . . .
8	Deep-sea fishing ground off Orkney.	H . . .
9	Kind of antelope.	I . . . .
10	Driver of a hackney coach in Ireland.	J . . . . .
11	Currency of Malawi.	K . . . . .
12	Study of shores.	L . . . .
13	Marzipan.	M . . . .
14	Small West African cat.	N . . . . . .
15	Rank, stinking.	O . . .
16	Roman magistrate.	P . . . . . .
17	Genus of tree, oaks.	Q . . . . . .
18	The former name of Yangon.	R . . . . . .
19	Currency of Ecuador.	S . . . .
20	Painting on a wall or ceiling.	T . . . .
21	Roman Catholic religious order.	U . . . .
22	Central shrine of Indian temple.	V . . . . .
23	The gudgeon.	W . . . . .
24	Pertaining to animal life.	Z . . .

SEVENTY-NINE

1　Airline of Italy, code name AZ.　A . . . .

2　Married name of the 19th-century writer on cookery, Isabella Mary Mayson.　B . . . . .

3　What is cayman a type of?　C . . . .

4　Who, in Greek mythology, was turned into the laurel which became Apollo's sacred tree?　D . . . . .

5　In Nepali it is Sagarmatha and in Chinese Qomolangha Feng (sacred mother of waters) . What is its English name?　E . . . . . .

6　Adjective which refers to a country's treasury, finances or tax matters.　F . . . . .

7　Australian feminist and author of *The Female Eunuch* (1970).　G . . . .

8　To what do the terms bradyeardia, tachycardia and palpitation refer?　H . . . .

9　A lamp which produces visible light from a heated source or filament.　I . . . .

10　What did Chinese poets call the 'concentrated essence of love'?　J . . .

11　What predominantly Irish Christian name means 'small dark one'?　K . . . . .

12　What is kept in a chest or wooden trunk called a kist?　L . . . .

13　Group or system regarded as a small representation of the whole world.　M . . . .

14　What type of arched prefabricated shelter was named after a 19th–20th-century British engineer?　N . . . . .

15　Who was the celebrated mythical musician of Thrace?　O . . . . . .

16 The names Jeremiah and Cassandra are connected with what type of people? P . . . .

17 What adjective, meaning romantically idealistic, is after the eponymous hero of a series of books by Cervantes? Q . . . .

18 Who was the British colonial administrator who first established a British settlement at Singapore? R . . . . . .

19 What was the former name of Ho Chi Minh City? S . . . . .

20 Herb with sweet leaves used in vinegar and mayonnaise. T . . . .

21 A coaching-team consisting of a pair of horses with a third horse in front. U . . . . . .

22 The Latin version of the Bible, dating from the 4th century AD. V . . . . . .

23 Odobenid is the related adjective for which creature? W . . . . .

24 Turquoise and which other gemstone are associated with the month of December? Z . . . . .

EIGHTY

1	The elbow.	A . . . .
2	Group of quail.	B . . .
3	Hungarian dance.	C . . . . . .
4	Currency of Gambia.	D . . . . .
5	Sword-shaped.	E . . . .
6	Prepared fibre.	F . . . . . .
7	Clumsy soldier.	G . . . . .
8	Cuban dance in slow time.	H . . . .
9	Useless.	I . . . . . .

10	Kind of early pear.	J . . . .
11	The shrew in *The Taming of the Shrew*.	K . . . .
12	Fast leaping dance.	L . . . . . .
13	Woman displaying clothes.	M . . . .
14	Australian edible red fish.	N . . . .
15	Having four legs.	O . . . .
16	Used to move a log.	P . . . . .
17	A curl.	Q . . . .
18	A farthing.	R . . . .
19	Group of mallard.	S . . .
20	Speed.	T . . .
21	Nettle-rash.	U . . . .
22	Warming of a rock.	V . . . .
23	Annual dinner in a printing office.	W . . . .
24	Process of fermentation.	Z . . . . . .

EIGHTY-ONE

1 Mustapha Kemal, elected President of Turkey in August 1923, was better known by what name?   A . . . . . .

2 What profession was taken up by Butch Cassidy of 'Butch Cassidy and the Sundance Kid' fame?   B . . . . . .

3 What is 'Fuller's earth'?   C . . .

4 Who did George Bush defeat to become US President in 1988?   D . . . . . .

5 The home of the blessed dead in Greek mythology.   E . . . . . .

6 What type of gold is pyrite?   F . . . .

7   Surname of oboist Léon, his brother (the conductor) Eugène, and sisters (both harpists) Marie and Sidonie?   G. . . . . . .

8   What have you got if you are suffering from singultus?   H. . . . . .

9   Which city was known as Byzantium from 660BC–AD330?   I. . . . . . .

10   A wine bottle holding 10–12 quarts.   J. . . . . . .

11   Gadget invented in 1816 by Sir David Brewster.   K. . . . .

12   What is the name of the lighthouse off Land's End?   L. . . . .

13   Who was the Greek God of Sleep and Dreams?   M. . . . . . .

14   What are lumber, sacral, maxilliary, median, ulnar, digital and tibial names of?   N. . . . .

15   Animal also known as painted leopard or tigrillo.   O. . . . .

16   What does an eretephobiac fear?   P. . .

17   A type of square dance.   Q. . . . .

18   Whose wife was Bessy Throckmorton?   R. . . . . .

19   What is a 'whooper' a type of?   S. . .

20   What adjective pertains to the Muse of Dancing?   T. . . . .

21   Business term for breaking up a conglomerate after taking it over, and keeping only the core business.   U. . . . . . .

22   What word means that a dish is served with white grapes?   V. . . . .

23   What is logophobia fear of?   W. . . .

24   The Kariba Dam stands on which river?   Z. . . . . .

1	Quickening pace in music.	A..........
2	Group of hunters.	B....
3	Currency of Brazil.	C.......
4	Watercourse with steep sides.	D....
5	A journey or circuit.	E...
6	A paper match.	F......
7	Praise exultantly.	G......
8	A rope with a loop used on a horse.	H........
9	In the same place.	I.....
10	Sedan chair.	J.....
11	Japanese traditional drama.	K.....
12	Fear of string.	L...........
13	North Indian tree.	M.........
14	Small sweet orange-like mandarin.	N.......
15	Pertaining to kitchen gardens.	O......
16	Founder of the Boy Scouts.	P.....
17	A girl.	Q....
18	Town hall in Germany.	R......
19	A number that is subtracted.	S.........
20	The Norse god of battle.	T..
21	Consisting of only one letter.	U.........
22	Pertaining to dress.	V.......
23	Subterranean chamber.	W...
24	Former King of Albania.	Z..

EIGHTY-THREE

1 Who succeeded Hirohito as Emperor of
Japan in 1989?   A......

2 Lizzie, who according to the rhyme 'gave her mother forty whacks' and 'her father forty-one'.   B.....

3 What are Madeleines and Brownies types of?   C....

4 Another name for the Ten Commandments.   D........

5 Of what is oology the study?   E...

6 Dog, buck, jack and hob are all recognised male names for which creature?   F.....

7 What type of dome was invented by Buckminster Fuller in the 1950s?   G.......

8 According to Longfellow, which Indian was married to Minnehaha?   H.......

9 What is entomophobia fear of?   I......

10 Poem by Lewis Carroll in *Through the Looking Glass*.   J..........

11 The 120-member Israeli Parliament.   K......

12 Native to Australia, what is a goanna a type of?   L.....

13 Of what is pennyroyal a species?   M...

14 Toppled Panamanian dictator convicted in America for drug trafficking and racketeering.   N......

15 An 800th anniversary.   O..........

16 What was the name of the dog that found football's Jules Rimet trophy (the World Cup) after it was stolen in 1966?   P......

17 A pigtail.   Q....

18 In music, what sort of setting would the orchestral piece 'pastorale' suggest?   R....

19 What is meant by the mathematical sign Σ?   S........

20 Who collaborated with Elton John writing songs, including 'Rocket Man' and 'Goodbye Yellow Brick Road'?   T . . . . .

21 Ventilation shaft in a mine.   U . . . . .

22 Who was the US industrialist who developed the current scoring system for contract bridge?   V . . . .

23 Maxim de —— was the hero of the Daphne du Maurier novel *Rebecca*.   W . . . . .

24 Animal-worship.   Z . . . .

EIGHTY-FOUR

1	Having no trace of life.	A . . . .
2	Currency of Panama.	B . . . . .
3	Spanish dance.	C . . . .
4	Study of trees.	D . . . .
5	One of four officers of Yeomen of the Guard.	E . . .
6	A bond in brickwork.	F . . . . .
7	Kind of legging.	G . . . . .
8	A Muslim who journeys to Mecca.	H . . . .
9	Pertaining to fishes.	I . . . .
10	Oaten bread.	J . . . . . .
11	Small Malayan tree.	K . . . .
12	Austrian dance.	L . . . . . .
13	Kitchen wench.	M . . . . .
14	Small piece of mutton.	N . . . .
15	Stiff, light, transparent muslin.	O . . . .
16	Relative humidity measured by this.	P . . . .
17	Evasion of the point.	Q . . . . . .
18	Noise of drum beating.	R . . . .

19	Name for being cross-eyed.	S.........
20	Thick paste of sesame seeds.	T.....
21	Formerly.	U.......
22	A herb or shrub.	V.......
23	A univalve many-whorled shell.	W.........
24	Isle of cloves.	Z.......

EIGHTY-FIVE

1 Liquorice-flavoured spice used in pie fillings.
A......

2 Rope with weights attached, used in South Africa for catching cattle by snaring their legs.
B....

3 Who was poisoned by his fourth wife Agrippina?
C.......

4 With what is a cynomaniac obsessed?
D...

5 Of what is psephology the study?
E........

6 An ancient Roman market-place or square.
F....

7 French inventor, and famous name of the cinema, who was responsible for the first talking pictures, demonstrated at Paris in 1910.
G......

8 What is the name of the island which is divided between the Dominican Republic and Haiti?
H.........

9 Alloy containing 65 per cent iron and 35 per cent nickel.
I....

10 A slang term for a piano.
J.....

11 Which city in Sri Lanka is called the 'city of four hills'?
K....

12 British Labour politician, founder of

the *Daily Herald* and grandfather of a
well-known stage, screen and television
actress.   L.......

13   What does a phillumenist collect?   M.........

14   What was the name of the US nuclear
submarine which travelled under the North
Polar ice-cap in 1958?   N.......

15   Chemical element symbol OS.   O.....

16   A sentence which contains every
letter of the alphabet, for example, 'the
quick brown fox jumps over the lazy dog'.   P......

17   A plane figure having 15 sides and 15
angles.   Q..........

18   Personality test in which the subject
interprets abstract ink blots.   R........

19   Who built the first successful
helicopter in 1939?   S.......

20   What was invented by J .R . Whinfield
and J .T . Dickson in England in 1946?   T.......

21   The Central American black vulture.   U....

22   Mexican cowboy or herdsman.   V......

23   Who was the Pretender to the English
throne who was executed in 1499?   W......

24   German optician whose factory at
Jena became noted for producing lenses
and microscopes.   Z....

EIGHTY-SIX

1   Without a head.   A.........
2   Conductor's baton.   B.......
3   Currency of Nicaragua.   C......
4   Funeral lament.   D....

5   A plant growing on another.   E . . . .
6   French hackney coach.   F . . . . .
7   Four-winged stream fly.   G . . . . . .
8   Ceremonial Maori dance.   H . . .
9   Fear of ideas.   I . . . .
10 Shin piece of armour.   J . . . .
11 A jackdaw.   K . .
12 The patron saint of writers.   L . . .
13 Pertaining to the cheek.   M . . . .
14 Yellow water-lily.   N . . . . .
15 Game of cards.   O . . . .
16 Greek peninsula.   P . . . .
17 A quibble.   Q . . . . . .
18 A rascal.   R . . . .
19 Soft-toned organ stop.   S . . . . . .
20 Chieftain's walking-stick.   T . . . . .
21 Entrails of a deer.   U . . . . .
22 A film of ice on rock.   V . . . . . .
23 The curlew.   W . . . .
24 Spanish dance.   Z . . . .

EIGHTY-SEVEN

1   Which poet wrote 'this is the night mail
crossing the border/bringing the cheque
and the postal order'?   A . . . .

2   Where in France did the R101 airship
crash in 1930?   B . . . . . .

3   What does a cromophobiac fear?   C . . . . . .

4   A Russian open horse-drawn carriage. D . . . . . .

5   Ugandan town which, in 1976, was the scene of a dramatic rescue of Israelis whose plane had been hijacked by terrorists.

E . . . . . .

6   To what do piscary laws refer?

F . . . . . .

7   Who, in 1935, founded the American Institute of Public Opinion?

G . . . . .

8   Which Cambridgeshire town was the birthplace of Oliver Cromwell?

H . . . .

9   A solid figure having 20 plane sides.

I . . . .

10   An ornamental pot for growing flowers.

J . . . .

11   The Japanese martial art of sword fighting now practised with bamboo swords called shiani.

K . . . .

12   Who was the husband of Lady Godiva?

L . . . . . .

13   Doubling-up system in gambling, especially at roulette.

M . . . .

14   The index of stocks and shares prices on the Tokyo stock exchange.

N . . . . .

15   What is the name of the reference sign † used to indicate footnotes?

O . . . . . .

16   Seventeenth-century French mathematician who gave his name to a triangular arrangement of numbers.

P . . . . .

17   South African ass-like animal.

Q . . . . .

18   The name of Gerald Ford's vice-president from 1974–1977.

R . . . .

19   The highest order of angels.

S . . . .

20   Where was the swashbuckling film star Errol Flynn born?

T . . . .

21   Snail, whelk or similar mollusc having a single shell.

U . . . .

22	The act that created the Prohibition era in America in the 1920s.	V . . . .
23	Of what is polemology the study?	W . . .
24	The related adjective for zebra.	Z . . . . . .

1	Distilled spirit from the East.	A . . .
2	Fear of thunder.	B . . . .
3	Study of shells.	C . . . .
4	Group of swine.	D . . . .
5	Squadron of planes.	E . . . .
6	A brooch.	F . . . . . .
7	Indian ruler.	G . . . . . .
8	A Muslim physician.	H . . . . .
9	The lower curve of an arch.	I . . . .
10	Dish consisting of meat, sea food, rice, onions.	J . . . .
11	Japanese basket work.	K . . .
12	A common finch.	L . . . . .
13	Tights for ballet dancer.	M . . . . . .
14	Short-horned Indian antelope.	N . . . . . .
15	Conspiracy of silence.	O . . . . .
16	Unit of intensity of sound.	P . . .
17	Crossbow bolt or arrow.	Q . . . . . .
18	Having many small branches.	R . . . .
19	Group of apes.	S . . . .
20	New Zealand gannet.	T . . . . .
21	Eighth day of feast.	U . . .
22	A sentinel.	V . . . . . .
23	Small West African weaver bird.	W . . . . .

24   What is meant by the suffix -ling?   Y . . . .

EIGHTY-NINE

1   What is a Morris column used for?   A . . . .

2   Who became President of USSR in May
1960?   B . . . .

3   Planetary satellite of Pluto, discovered
1978.   C . . . . .

4   What does a rupophobiac fear?   D . . .

5   Scottish island historically associated
with the clan MacDonald.   E . . .

6   A tarboosh is one.   F . .

7   The land in Egypt given by Pharoah to
the Israelites to dwell in.   G . . . . .

8   Unit of weight equal to 100 grams.   H . . . .

9   Shimmering with a rainbow-like effect.   I . . . .

10   One-time partner of comedian Ben
Warris.   J . . . .

11   Two-masted fore-and-aft-rigged
sailing vessel.   K . . . .

12   American political columnist who
coined the phrase 'The Cold War'.   L . . . .

13   Broad, heavy knife originating from
Central and South America.   M . . . . . .

14   A blissful state of freedom from care.   N . . . . . .

15   What type of front does the symbol
▲▲▲ signify in meteorology?   O . . . .

16   Who was the eponymous heroine of a
1913 Eleanor Porter novel whose name
has become synonymous with excessive
optimism?   P . . . .

17   An arrangement of five things in a

square or rectangle with one at each corner
and one in the middle.   Q . . . .

18   Italian renaissance painter whose
works include *La Donna Valeta* and *The
Marriage of the Virgin*.   R . . . . . .

19   In which film of 1967 did Julie
Andrews play Gertrude Lawrence?   S . . .

20   Prime Minister of Canada from
1968–1979 and 1980–1984.   T . . . . . .

21   Evergreen Malaysian tree whose latex
is used to make arrow poison.   U . . .

22   In music, what is meant by the term
'con brio'?   V . . . .

23   In what is an oenologist an expert?   W . . .

24   Book of the Old Testament .   Z . . . .

NINETY

1	Globular flask with two handles.	A . . . . .
2	Group of ducks.	B . . . .
3	A type of bear.	C . . . . .
4	Name of the Japanese parliament.	D . . .
5	Find an anagram of EVIL'S AGENTS.	E . . . .
6	Capable of being moulded.	F . . . . . .
7	African lemur.	G . . . . .
8	Resembling common salt.	H . . . . .
9	East Indian pheasant.	I . . . . . .
10	Game similar to pelota.	J . . / . . . .
11	God of love.	K . . .
12	Old name for Portugal.	L . . . .
13	Aboriginal sling for a child.	M . . .
14	South American beaver.	N . . . . .

15	Pertaining to the shoulder-blades.	O . . . .
16	Currency of Macao.	P . . . . .
17	Peruvian bark.	Q . . . .
18	In a crazy state.	R . . . .
19	Having the ratio of a cube to a square.	S . . . .
20	Indian fan palm.	T . . . . . .
21	The act of bowing.	U . . . . .
22	A small inlet.	V . .
23	Furze, gorse.	W . . .
24	Currency of Zaire.	Z . . . .

NINETY-ONE

1	What is a dipsomaniac addicted to?	A . . . . . .
2	Porcine, suidian and suilling are all related adjectives for which animal?	B . . .
3	What are trefly, fleurée, patonce, potent, avellane and globical types of?	C . . . . . .
4	Canadian Prime Minister from 1957–1963.	D . . . .
5	What does the adjective palpebral refer to?	E . . . . . .
6	What are double loops, radial loops, arches, whorles and ulnar loops?	F . . . .
7	Who said, when asked what he thought of Western civilisation, 'I think it would be an excellent idea'?	G . . . . .
8	Thomas —— was the author of *Tom Brown's Schooldays*.	H . . . . .
9	What does a dikephobiac fear?	I . . . .
10	Name of the family tree showing Jesus' ancestry.	J . . . .

11	The official language of Cambodia.	K . . . .
12	Airline of Luxembourg, code name LG.	L . . . . .
13	What female Christian name means 'mighty battle-maiden'?	M . . . . . .
14	What, in mythology, are naiads, hamadryads and nereids?	N . . . . .
15	A lake formed from a U-shaped bend in a river.	O . . . .
16	What does a deltiologist collect?	P . . . .
17	A discharge or release from a debt.	Q . . . . . .
18	What do Americans call an estate agent?	R . . . . . .
19	What was the pseudonym of Herman Cyril McNeile (1888–1937), the creator of 'Bulldog Drummond'?	S . . . . .
20	What are keraunophobia, brontophobia and tonitrophobia all fear of?	T . . . . . .
21	Republic in Asia which became independent in 1991, capital Tashkent.	U . . . .
22	A vivid red colour.	V . . . .
23	What do xylophagous insects eat?	W . . .
24	Ancient Babylonian temple in the shape of a steep pyramid.	Z . . . .

NINETY-TWO

1	Wing-footed creature.	A . . . . .
2	Fear of walking.	B . . . .
3	The road runner bird.	C . . . .
4	A rhyming couplet.	D . . . . . .
5	Resembling a caterpillar.	E . . . .
6	Light covering of the neck of women.	F . . . .

7 Freshwater duck.	G......
8 A rope for lowering sails.	H......
9 New Zealand whitebait.	I.....
10 Revolt of the peasants in France.	J........
11 Small barrel.	K........
12 Name for speech defects.	L.........
13 Dark strong cigar.	M.....
14 Japanese descendant born in USA.	N....
15 Eating raw flesh.	O........
16 Afraid of swimming.	P............
17 Of the fifth degree.	Q......
18 Belonging to branches.	R......
19 Type of furniture.	S.......
20 A public function.	T......
21 Extinct wild ox.	U...
22 Botanist's collecting case.	V.......
23 A basket.	W......
24 A shrewish wife.	X.......

NINETY-THREE

1 What is the name of the US space shuttle which was first launched on 3 October 1985?	A.......
2 What is an Eskimo's nukluk a type of?	B...
3 What does a demophobiac fear?	C.....
4 Mobile platform for a film or video camera and its operator.	D....
5 A small island, especially in a river.	E...
6 Of what is pomology the study?	F.....

7 What plant is also called
Jack-go-to-bed-at-noon?   G . . . .

8 What shape is described as 'cordate'?   H . . . .

9 White metallic element at no . 77
symbol Ir.   I . . . . . .

10 Pertaining to the cheek-bone.   J . . . .

11 Strong, brown, wrapping-paper whose
name is taken from the German word for
strength.   K . . . .

12 What are eremiophobia, autophobia
and monophobia all fear of?   L . . . .

13 What word means either medieval
wood carvings found in churches or a
medieval dagger?   M . . . .

14 Lake in Mozambique, sometimes
known as the 'calendar lake' because it is
365 miles long and 52 miles across at its
widest point.   N . . . .

15 The back part of the head.   O . . . . . .

16 US general, byname 'Black Jack', who
gave his name to a nuclear missile.   P . . . .

17 A five-year period or fifth anniversary.   Q . . . .

18 What does a pluviometer measure?   R . . . .

19 In which fictional prison was the TV
comedy *Porridge* set?   S . . . .

20 What is the name of the large lake in
Peru?   T . . . .

21 A written composition that makes use
of only one vowel in all its words.   U . . . .

22 The scientific study of volcanoes.   V . . . .

23 What surname was shared by US
artist James Abbott McNeill and British
artist Rex?   W . . . .

24 Japanese admiral responsible for the
attack on Pearl Harbor in 1941.   Y . . . .

---

NINETY-FOUR

1   Pertaining to the belly.   A . . . . .
2   Edward Teach known as.   B . . . .
3   Fear of sea swell.   C . . . .
4   Currency of Morocco.   D . . . . .
5   A Swiss cheese.   E . . . .
6   Potter's clay.   F . . . .
7   A simpleton.   G . . .
8   Wood nymph.   H . . . .
9   A fillet worn by priests.   I . . . . .
10 Gold coin struck in reign of James I.   J . . . . . .
11 A tantrum.   K . . . . . .
12 Gulliver's first name.   L . . . . .
13 Spot on the skin.   M . . . . .
14 Redundancy.   N . . . . . .
15 The shoulder-blade.   O . . . .
16 Ornamental flower-bed.   P . . . . . .
17 A fantasy.   Q . . . .
18 Dish of eggs, cheese and breadcrumbs.   R . . . . . .
19 What is an augur?   S . . . .
20 American bird.   T . . . . . .
21 Who is Dismas patron saint of?   U . . . .
22 Smallpox.   V . . . . . .
23 The bilberry.   W . . . .
24 Exclusion of foreigners from a
country.   X . . . .

NINETY-FIVE

1   Who was the giant watchman in Greek mythology with 100 eyes?

A . . . .

2   Who assassinated British Prime Minister Spencer Perceval in 1812?

B . . . .

3   Whose last words were 'My design is to make what haste I can to be gone'?

C . . . .

4   Tower of volcanic rock which is a US national monument in Wyoming used as a setting for the movie *Close Encounters of a Third Kind.*

D . . . . .

5   Fear of work.

E . . . .

6   What is an anthomaniac addicted to?

F . . . . . .

7   Grotesque beasts originally carved on church walls to act as water-spouts.

G . . . .

8   Figure of speech where an exaggeration is made for emphasis, for example, 'I could drink a well dry'.

H . . . .

9   Which industrial, historical town is known as the birthplace of England's industrial revolution?

I . . . .

10   Judo suit worn during contests.

J . . . . .

11   Which astronomer formulated laws concerning the revolution of planets around the Sun?

K . . . . .

12   What is philology the study of?

L . . . .

13   The Israeli secret service.

M . . . . .

14   In which mythological country did C.S. Lewis set his novel *The Lion, The Witch and the Wardrobe?*

N . . . . .

15   What male Christian name is the Italian form of Roland?

O . . . . . .

16 Who, in AD62, did the Emperor Nero marry?   P . . . . . .

17 An ancient roman two-wheeled chariot drawn by four horses abreast.   Q . . . .

18 The poison used to murder Bulgarian broadcaster Georgei Markov in London in 1978.   R . . . .

19 What is tacophobia fear of?   S . . . .

20 Island group in the South West Pacific, formerly called Ellis Islands.   T . . . . .

21 The killing of one's wife.   U . . . .

22 The production of live young rather than eggs.   V . . . .

23 To what do the words leniferous, flocculent and batting all refer?   W . . .

24 Element with atomic no . 40 and symbol Zr.   Z . . . .

NINETY-SIX

1   Wing-shaped.   A . . . . . .
2   Afraid of frogs.   B. . . . .
3   Female singer.   C . . . .
4   Instrument for measuring density of gas.   D . . . .
5   Having pairs of feet equal.   E . . . .
6   The polecat.   F . . . . . .
7   Strolling beggar.   G . . . .
8   Hooked.   H . . . . .
9   A reporter.   I . ./ . . . .
10 Squirrel-like South American monkey.   J . . . . . .
11 Tomb formed by stone clubs.   K . . . .

12	Defensive encampment.	L . . . . .
13	Short horizontal line over a vowel.	M . . . . .
14	Pertaining to Noah.	N . . . .
15	Variety of black tea.	O . . . .
16	Bridge of stringed instrument.	P . . . .
17	Tortilla filled with cheese.	Q . . . .
18	Attired.	R . . .
19	Shaped like a shield.	S . . . .
20	Small mammal-like hedgehog.	T . . . . .
21	Egyptian serpent emblem.	U . . . . . .
22	A rampart.	V . . . . .
23	The rowan tree.	W . . . . .
24	Cross-fertilisation.	X . . . .

NINETY-SEVEN

1   What was the name of the British missionary in China portrayed by Ingrid Bergman in *The Inn of the Sixth Happiness*?   A . . . . . .

2   What are you doing if you are in a state of erubescence?   B . . . .

3   What was invented by Jacques Brandenberger in Switzerland in 1908?   C . . . .

4   What are scotophobia, nyctophobia, achluophobia and lygophobia all fear of?   D . . .

5   The second natural satellite of Jupiter discovered by Galileo in 1610.   E . . . . .

6   Obstruction of legislation by means of delaying tactics such as lengthy speeches.   F . . . .

7   What does a nelophobiac fear?   G . . . .

8   How was Henry Percy, who fell fighting against Henry IV at Shrewsbury, otherwise known?   H . . . . . .

9   Which author wrote *Rip Van Winkle* and *The Legend of Sleepy Hollow* under the pseudonym of Geoffrey Crayon?   I . . . . .

10   The philosophy of law.   J . . . .

11   Which Pacific republic of thirty-three coral islands was formerly called The Gilbert Islands?   K . . . .

12   What is mythomania addiction to?   L . . . .

13   Of what is bryology the study?   M . . . . .

14   Who was the Scottish mathematician who invented logarithms?   N . . . . .

15   Airport to the south of Paris.   O . . .

16   To what does the adjective pavonine refer?   P . . . . . .

17   A riding whip with short handle and long lash.   Q . . . .

18   The active form of vitamin A found in margarines, oily fish and dairy fats.   R . . . . . .

19   What shape is allantoid?   S . . . . . .

20   What name in Greek originally meant 'manifestation of God'?   T . . . . . .

21   The act of burning.   U . . . . .

22   A chronic invalid or hypochondriac.   V . . . .

23   Who was the 13th-century Earl known as the Kingmaker?   W . . . . . .

24   Who were the race of brutish ape-like people in Swift's *Gulliver's Travels*?   Y . . . . .

1	Free from echoes.	A . . . .
2	Turkish heel-length slipper.	B . . . .
3	Fear of going to bed.	C . . . .
4	Kind of plover.	D . . . .
5	Residential area outside the suburbs.	E . . . . . .
6	A small fort.	F . . . .
7	Tax on salt in France.	G . . . . . .
8	Sweating.	H . . . .
9	An animal living in the abode of another.	I . . . .
10	Type of goat found in Ethiopia.	J . . .
11	A ravine.	K . . . .
12	Volcanic ash.	L . . . . . .
13	Kind of granite.	M . . . .
14	Great bat.	N . . . . . .
15	Kind of moulding.	O . . . .
16	A person who fears leaves.	P . . . .
17	Set of four.	Q . . . .
18	Type of chicory from Italy.	R . . . .
19	Person who studies fleas.	S . . . .
20	Tapestry.	T . . . .
21	Of the elm.	U . . . .
22	A groove or furrow.	V . . . .
23	Type of frankfurter.	W . . . . .
24	A morbid liking for foreign things.	X . . . .

1   'The Valley' is the capital of which British colony of the Leeward Islands?   A . . . .

2   Slang term for a secret agent who pays bribes.   B . . . . .

3   The dried kernel of the coconut.   C . . . .

4   A picture consisting of two panels, hinged like the pages of a book.   D . . . . . .

5   The theological study of the nature of the Christian church.   E . . . .

6   What does a doraphobiac fear?   F . .

7   Who was the cupbearer of the gods in Greek mythology?   G . . . .

8   Creature produced by mating a male horse with a female donkey.   H . . . .

9   A written decree of a Muslim ruler.   I . . . .

10   Statesman who helped found Pakistan in 1947.   J . . . . .

11   Whip previously used as an instrument of punishment in Russia.   K . . . .

12   What is the eyepiece or magnifying glass called, as used by a jeweller?   L . . . .

13   What is a quizzing glass an archaic term for?   M . . . . . .

14   Who was the Greek Goddess of Victory?   N . . .

15   On which Hawaiian island was Pearl Harbor?   O . . .

16   Swedish Prime Minister assassinated in 1986.   P . . . .

17   A square or diamond-shaped pane of glass used in lattice-windows.   Q . . . . . .

18 What are monopitch, gambrel and jerkin types of?   R . . . .

19 Of what is pedology the study?   S . . .

20 What shape is napiform?   T . . . . .

21 Resembling a grape.   U . . . . .

22 Genus of butterfly which includes Red Admiral and Camberwell Beauty.   V . . . . . .

23 Dragon with wings and a serpent's tail, as in heraldry.   W . . . . .

24 Figure of speech, for example, 'he held his tongue and his promise'.   Z . . . . .

ONE HUNDRED

1	A person in fear of bees.	A . . . .
2	Open carriage.	B . . . . . .
3	Winged staff of Mercury.	C . . . .
4	Who wrote *Lucia di Lammermoor*?	D . . . .
5	Having prickly skin.	E . . . .
6	Having a deeply cleft beak.	F . . . .
7	Flat river vessel.	G . . . . . .
8	The kingfisher.	H . . . . . .
9	An isolated steep rocky hill.	I . . . .
10	Light coat of armour.	J . . . .
11	Hard swelling on trunk of tree.	K . . .
12	West Indian dance.	L . . . .
13	A device to transmit and receive data.	M . . . .
14	Province of a country.	N . . .
15	Contemplating your navel.	O . . . .
16	Igneous rock of feldspar.	P . . . .
17	Having five angles.	Q . . . .

18 A number from which a root is to be extracted.   R . . . .

19 Movement in music that in Italian means joke.   S . . . . . .

20 A tangerine.   T . . . . . .

21 What is the opposite of dystopia?   U . . . . .

22 Lively.   V . . . .

23 Dogwood tree.   W . . . .

24 Christian rule of fasting.   X . . . .

Solutions

ONE

1 Acorn 2 Berlin 3 *Casablanca* 4 Delilah 5 Elk 6 Fats 7 Goons
8 Hogmanay 9 Idaho 10 Jelly 11 Kew 12 Lama 13 Mars
14 Nelson 15 Ounce 16 Pearl 17 Queen 18 Robin 19 Scouts
20 Twister 21 Underwriter 22 Ventriloquism 23 Waterloo
24 Yachts

10–12	Fair
13–17	Good
18–21	Very good
22–24	Excellent

TWO

1 Abbess 2 Ballad 3 Colt 4 Davits 5 Edam 6 Foxtrot 7 Guitar
8 Herd 9 Iraq 10 Jutland 11 Kip 12 Louvre 13 Morse
14 Nausea 15 Ottawa 16 Pompeii 17 Quickstep 18 Rwanda
19 Singapore 20 Turban 21 Unkindness 22 Vellum
23 Waterman 24 Yawl

10–12	Fair
13–17	Good
18–21	Very good
22–24	Excellent

THREE

1 Arson 2 Battleships 3 Cupid 4 David 5 Excalibur 6 Four
7 Grass 8 Horoscope 9 Ivan 10 Jigsaw 11 Kenya 12 Lent
13 Millipede 14 Netball 15 Oxford 16 Parallel 17 Quart
18 Rainbow 19 Shamrock 20 Tudor 21 Utah 22 Venison
23 Woodwind 24 Yeti

10–12	Fair
13–17	Good
18–21	Very good
22–24	Excellent

FOUR

1 Acme 2 Bolero 3 Company 4 Dodo 5 Emu 6 Fathom
7 Gillette 8 Homicide 9 Impeach 10 Joust 11 Karloff
12 Litany 13 Mexico 14 Nation 15 Opossum 16 Peso 17 Quiz
18 Rosé 19 Soprano 20 Toga 21 Udder 22 Vendetta
23 Wickets 24 Yen

10–12	Fair
13–17	Good
18–21	Very good
22–24	Excellent

FIVE

1 Accordion 2 Beatles 3 Crab 4 Derby 5 Emerald 6 Florin
7 Gladstone 8 Hammerstein 9 Iceland 10 Judith 11 Kennedy
12 Love 13 Micawber 14 Norway 15 Omnibus
16 Palindromes 17 Quarry 18 Rhinoceros 19 Stephen
20 Trilogy 21 Universities 22 Verdi 23 Windermere
24 Xerography

10–12	Fair
13–17	Good
18–21	Very good
22–24	Excellent

SIX

1 Adze 2 Brotherhood 3 Caber 4 Doxy 5 Epée 6 Franklin
7 Goodyear 8 Harmonica 9 Ingle 10 Jackal 11 Kaffir
12 Lorgnette 13 Morris 14 Neology 15 Oolong 16 Pascal
17 Quicksilver 18 Rand 19 Seine 20 Tsetse 21 Udometer
22 Vincent 23 Wedge 24 Younker

10–12 Fair
13–17 Good
18–21 Very good
22–24 Excellent

SEVEN

1 Adonis 2 Barrie 3 Crotchet 4 Dutch 5 Edison 6 Facsimile
7 Gemini 8 Highlighter 9 Idiot 10 Jersey 11 Knives 12 Louis
13 Methuselah 14 Nebraska 15 Orange 16 Pentathlon
17 Quadruped 18 Romanov 19 Sovereign 20 Trappist
21 Unfathomable 22 Verbatim 23 Wimbledon 24 Yak

10–12 Fair
13–16 Good
17–20 Very good
21–24 Excellent

EIGHT

1 Anon 2 Battery 3 Cohort 4 Drachma 5 Escargot
6 Flamenco 7 Galley 8 Highgate 9 Ingot 10 Jacuzzi 11 Kedge
12 Languages 13 Montevideo 14 Nemesis 15 Otis 16 Piquet
17 Quarter 18 Regicide 19 Shrike 20 Troop 21 Ulster
22 Vicar 23 Wolfram 24 Yorkie

10–12 Fair
13–16 Good
17–20 Very good
21–24 Excellent

NINE

1 Ancestors 2 Buster 3 Christopher 4 Degree 5 Eclipse
6 Freud 7 Geordie 8 Health 9 Iota 10 Jolson 11 Khartoum
12 Llama 13 Morse 14 Navratilova 15 Oasis 16 Pelican
17 Queensberry 18 Rubber 19 Sooty 20 Tibet 21 Uranium
22 Veteran 23 Westminster 24 Yeast

10–12	Fair
13–16	Good
17–20	Very good
21–24	Excellent

TEN

1 Affray 2 Board 3 Coney 4 Doge 5 Escutcheon 6 Fuschia
7 Gatling 8 Hillock 9 Infest 10 Jasper 11 Köchel 12 Last
13 Moa 14 Napier 15 Orkneys 16 Peccary 17 Quintic
18 Ruck 19 Squad 20 Toxophilite 21 Ultramarine 22 Vervet
23 Won 24 Yulan

10–12	Fair
13–16	Good
17–20	Very good
21–24	Excellent

ELEVEN

1 Argonauts 2 Bacall 3 Chamberlain 4 Davy 5 Eden 6 Freezy
7 Glee 8 Hollywood 9 ITMA 10 Jakarta 11 Kimberley
12 Leveret 13 Mouse 14 Noddy 15 Overpass 16 Potassium
17 Quire 18 Romany 19 Solidarity 20 Thirty 21 Urban
22 Violinist 23 Woolsack 24 Zara

9–11	Fair
12–15	Good
16–19	Very good
20–24	Excellent

TWELVE

1 Airedale 2 Batch 3 Crampon 4 Daimler 5 Esparto 6 Fiasco
7 Gew-gaw 8 Herring 9 Inertia 10 Jingoism 11 Kinesis
12 Lackey 13 Mozart 14 Nabob 15 Orange 16 Pentad
17 Quarto 18 Rial 19 Schick 20 Troupe 21 Ursine
22 Velodrome 23 Wales 24 Yokel

  9–11   Fair
12–15   Good
16–19   Very good
20–24   Excellent

THIRTEEN

1 Atlas 2 Byte 3 Carnarvon 4 Downing 5 Eighth 6 Force
7 Gable 8 Handlebar 9 Ibex 10 Juliana 11 Kingsley
12 Liberia 13 Ming 14 Nehru 15 Ohm 16 Parker
17 Quicksand 18 Ryder 19 Sistine 20 Tarzan
21 Untouchables 22 Vaudeville 23 Wok 24 Yashmak

  9–11   Fair
12–15   Good
16–19   Very good
20–24   Excellent

FOURTEEN

1 Alcove 2 Bouquet 3 Crevasse 4 Doubloon 5 Espresso
6 Flamingo 7 Giganticide 8 Hunt 9 Insipid 10 Jinn 11 Kitsch
12 Lapidary 13 Masse 14 Natant 15 Obeisance 16 Peso
17 Questor 18 Rollerskating 19 Steppes 20 Throng
21 Unkempt 22 Viperine 23 Whirlwind 24 Yammer

  9–11   Fair
12–15   Good
16–19   Very good
20–24   Excellent

FIFTEEN

1 Autobahn 2 Bristow 3 Checkers 4 Dizzy 5 Electric
6 Farthing 7 Garbo 8 Halifax 9 Irangate 10 Joey 11 Koran
12 Lamour 13 Marx 14 Neptune 15 Oil 16 Patton
17 Quarterdeck 18 Rodent 19 Silver 20 *Tosca* 21 Unarmed
22 Venezuela 23 Windsor 24 Yield

9–11	Fair
12–15	Good
16–19	Very good
20–24	Excellent

SIXTEEN

1 Anchovy 2 Bronze 3 Crinoline 4 Dong 5 Estuary 6 Fado
7 Gules 8 Horde 9 Isosceles 10 Junta 11 Kodiak 12 Lariat
13 Micrology 14 Neve 15 Obtuse 16 Paprika 17 Quant
18 Ratling 19 Styx 20 Teenology 21 Umpteen 22 Volute
23 Waddy 24 Zouave

9–11	Fair
12–15	Good
16–19	Very good
20–24	Excellent

SEVENTEEN

1 Allah 2 Budapest 3 Cain 4 Decimeter 5 Emmerdale 6 Fairy
7 Grampian 8 Hacker 9 Iris 10 Joist 11 Kissinger 12 Limbo
13 Mary 14 Nelson 15 Omega 16 Pasta 17 Quadrilateral
18 Romulus 19 Superbowl 20 Thelma 21 Unsolicited
22 Vesuvius 23 Watergate 24 Yoga

9–11	Fair
12–14	Good
15–18	Very good
19–24	Excellent

EIGHTEEN

1 Ambulate   2 Balsa   3 Croquet   4 Dinar   5 Emu   6 Flugel
7 Galliard   8 Head   9 Icebergs   10 Juniper   11 Kopje   12 Larynx
13 Marsala   14 Nog   15 Ocular   16 Pedology   17 Quiddity
18 Regalia 19 Shogun   20 Tiding   21 Utensil   22 Vitus
23 Waffle   24 Zounds

9–11	Fair
12–14	Good
15–18	Very good
19–24	Excellent

NINETEEN

1 Archimedes   2 Barbary   3 Cleveland   4 Drapes   5 Evita   6 Five
7 Giddy   8 Hardy   9 Isaac   10 Jitterbug   11 Kensington   12 Lime
13 Masefield   14 Nottingham   15 Origami   16 Pope   17 Quebec
18 Rodin   19 Salome   20 Tonne   21 Ulysses   22 Vacuum
23 Wayne   24 Zulu

9–11	Fair
12–14	Good
15–18	Very good
19–24	Excellent

TWENTY

1 Adobe   2 Bandanna   3 Cloth   4 Dolman   5 Egret   6 Fandango
7 Greenland   8 Hover   9 Impi   10 Jesuit   11 Krait   12 Lassitude
13 Marathon   14 Numbers   15 Oink   16 Pathology
17 Quidnunc   18 Rookery   19 Shilling   20 Theodolite   21 Ulst
22 Vulture   23 Wagga   24 Zuchetto

9–11	Fair
12–14	Good
15–18	Very good
19–24	Excellent

TWENTY-ONE

1 Anagrams 2 Boulder 3 Cluedo 4 Darwin 5 Epiphany
6 Frieze 7 Geranium 8 Hand 9 Ivy 10 Joint 11 Kellogg
12 Limpet 13 *Mayflower* 14 Neon 15 Otter 16 Pegasus
17 Quaver 18 Responsiblity 19 Sioux 20 Tuxedo 21 Ursa
22 Valletta 23 Waite 24 Yukon

8–10	Fair
11–13	Good
14–17	Very good
18–24	Excellent

TWENTY-TWO

1 Aerobics 2 Baillie 3 Colon 4 Den 5 Eland 6 Felicide
7 Glissando 8 Honshu 9 Incognito 10 Jugular 11 Karate
12 Libido 13 Mermaid's purse 14 Nuke 15 Oliver 16 Polonaise
17 Quiescent 18 Rummy 19 Sable 20 Tomato 21 Umbria
22 Valhalla 23 Wagon-lit 24 Zingaro

8–10	Fair
11–13	Good
14–17	Very good
18–24	Excellent

TWENTY-THREE

1 Aquarius 2 Bradman 3 Chaplin 4 Dinosaurs 5 Earth
6 Faucet 7 Gettysburg 8 *Halloween* 9 Isthmus 10 Jennifer
11 Kipling 12 Liverpool 13 Mexico 14 Napoleon 15 Orion
16 Pinkerton 17 Quakers 18 Reindeer 19 Sail 20 Thatcher
21 Ustinov 22 Vertigo 23 Water 24 Zambia

8–10	Fair
11–13	Good
14–17	Very good
18–24	Excellent

TWENTY-FOUR

1 Affidavit 2 Bermuda 3 Cap 4 Dingo 5 Earth 6 Forint
7 Gensing 8 Hals 9 Insignia 10 Jujube 11 Kapok 12 Lido
13 Martinique 14 Nonplus 15 Omnivore 16 Perseus
17 Quietus 18 Rivers 19 Sheep 20 Triangle 21 Uranus
22 Vacillate 23 Wallaby 24 Zinnia

8–10	Fair
11–13	Good
14–17	Very good
18–24	Excellent

TWENTY-FIVE

1 Advocaat 2 Blunt 3 Calamity 4 Distance 5 Etching 6 Fields
7 Ghana 8 Hoover 9 Ichthyology 10 James 11 Kiwi 12 Lucan
13 Mersey 14 Niven 15 Octagon 16 Prequel 17 Queensland
18 Ranger 19 Screws 20 Thirteen 21 Ukraine 22 Vera
23 Wilde 24 Yellowstone

8–10	Fair
11–13	Good
14–17	Very good
18–24	Excellent

TWENTY-SIX

1 Adagio 2 Bench 3 Coronet 4 Doberman 5 Epsilon 6 Fagotto
7 Genoa 8 Horse 9 Ideology 10 Jumbo 11 Kimono 12 Loam
13 Madder 14 Notary 15 Ordure 16 Pancake 17 Quentin
18 Retort 19 Sol 20 Tabard 21 Unicornus 22 Vanbrugh
23 Walloon 24 Zany

8–10	Fair
11–13	Good
14–17	Very good
18–24	Excellent

TWENTY-SEVEN

1 Atoll 2 Benbow 3 Cougar 4 Davis 5 Erie 6 Freetown
7 Goulash 8 Hebrew 9 Irish 10 Juno 11 Kaye 12 Lloyds
13 Maps 14 Nuremberg 15 Oval 16 Pandora 17 Quince
18 Rex 19 Spandau 20 Trident 21 Ultima 22 Victoria
23 Warsaw 24 Zimmer

 8–10 Fair
11–13 Good
14–17 Very good
18–24 Excellent

TWENTY-EIGHT

1 Albatross 2 Bandicoot 3 Craps 4 Ducal 5 Eight 6 Faunology
7 Gaff 8 Honey 9 Ilium 10 James 11 Kaama 12 Loch
13 Mandrill 14 Nave 15 Ooze 16 Persia 17 Quin 18 Remora
19 Sextet 20 Tabasco 21 Ursula 22 Viper 23 Wowser 24 Yapp

 8–10 Fair
11–13 Good
14–17 Very good
18–24 Excellent

TWENTY-NINE

1 Anaconda 2 Bolsheviks 3 Conrad 4 Dewar 5 Engines
6 Fencing 7 Gabriel 8 Hawke 9 Ipswich 10 Joseph 11 Kabul
12 Lincoln 13 Maori 14 Nose 15 Ontario 16 Presto
17 Quiche 18 Rumpole 19 Shorthand 20 Twitcher
21 Unpremeditated 22 Vicereine 23 Woggle 24 Zimbabwe

 8–10 Fair
11–13 Good
14–17 Very good
18–24 Excellent

THIRTY

1 Abyssinia 2 Bannock 3 Calypso 4 Ducat 5 Ecu 6 Franchise
7 Gaffer 8 Harvestman 9 Impale 10 Jabot 11 Kaka 12 Lucent
13 Mornay 14 Nephrology 15 Opine 16 Parsec 17 Queen
18 Rabat 19 Spinach 20 Tacit 21 Ubiquity 22 Voodoo
23 Wobbegong 24 Xanthic

8–10	Fair
11–13	Good
14–17	Very good
18–24	Excellent

THIRTY-ONE

1 Andorra 2 Bournville 3 Circus 4 Didgeridoo 5 Elgar
6 Feathers 7 Gaitskill 8 Haiti 9 Intelligence 10 June
11 Kentucky 12 Lodge 13 Melbourne 14 Nazareth 15 Oman
16 Pulitzer 17 Quasimodo 18 Roc 19 Solitaire 20 Tragedies
21 Usurer 22 Vintner 23 Wedge 24 Yankee

7–9	Fair
10–12	Good
13–16	Very good
17–24	Excellent

THIRTY-TWO

1 Ayah 2 Baba 3 Conjunctivitis 4 Dralon 5 Espadrille
6 Falcate 7 Gaga 8 Habitué 9 Inch 10 Jackpot 11 Kalong
12 Ludo 13 Motet 14 Nefertiti 15 Osier 16 Painters
17 Quinella 18 Rache 19 Shekel 20 Taciturn 21 Umber
22 Voracious 23 Warfarin 24 Xylem

7–9	Fair
10–12	Good
13–16	Very good
17–24	Excellent

THIRTY-THREE

1 Aldrin 2 Boyle's 3 Calais 4 Domesday 5 Echo 6 Fellini
7 Gavel 8 Hologram 9 Innsbruck 10 Jackson 11 Kilogram
12 Ladysmith 13 Madison 14 Nimbus 15 Ombudsman
16 Pleasure 17 Quarantine 18 Ragtime 19 Spooner 20 Tea
21 Urbane 22 Vindaloo 23 Warhol 24 Yuppie

7–9   Fair
10–12 Good
13–16 Very good
17–24 Excellent

THIRTY-FOUR

1 Azure 2 Barbet 3 Caballero 4 Duenna 5 Ecru 6 Faldstool
7 Gambrel 8 Haiku 9 Insomnia 10 Jackboot 11 Krona
12 Lulu 13 Muggins 14 Nacarat 15 Obvolute 16 Pentagram
17 Quinta 18 Raffia 19 Stud 20 Talbot 21 Uvula 22 Volatile
23 Wayfarer 24 Xyster

7–9   Fair
10–12 Good
13–16 Very good
17–24 Excellent

THIRTY-FIVE

1 Ants 2 Barnum 3 Candide 4 Dumas 5 Epicentre 6 Fangio
7 Grasmere 8 Hogarth 9 Inflation 10 Jacobean 11 Kohinoor
12 Lilliput 13 Matthew 14 Nicosia 15 Ottoman 16 Pedantic
17 Quail 18 Referendum 19 Stitches 20 Taiwan
21 Uniformity 22 Vadim 23 Wellington 24 Zeta

7–9   Fair
10–12 Good
13–16 Very good
17–24 Excellent

THIRTY-SIX

1 Ampersand 2 Bisque 3 Croquette 4 Dulcimer 5 Escudo
6 Fan-tan 7 Garrison 8 Hangar 9 Involute 10 Jackass
11 Kumasi 12 Lacuna 13 Macedoine 14 Nacelle 15 Ogive
16 Pompey 17 Quisling 18 Ramose 19 Steel 20 Talma
21 Upholster 22 Vogue 23 Wedlock 24 Yuan

7–9   Fair
10–12   Good
13–16   Very good
17–24   Excellent

THIRTY-SEVEN

1 Angles 2 Bernstein 3 Coleridge 4 Dundee 5 Emir
6 Fujiyama 7 Greece 8 Hutton 9 Indictment 10 Jenkins
11 Kookaburra 12 *Limelight* 13 McKinley 14 Nylon 15 Owens
16 Plough 17 Quadrant 18 Revere 19 Swagman 20 Tijuana
21 Unique 22 Vitamins 23 Wodehouse 24 Yonkers

7–9   Fair
10–12   Good
13–16   Very good
17–24   Excellent

THIRTY-EIGHT

1 Argot 2 Bireme 3 Cirrus 4 Dungaree 5 Erne 6 Fanzine
7 Grandee 8 Halma 9 Infuscate 10 Jeep 11 Krone 12 Lambda
13 Morocco 14 Nacho 15 Otology 16 Platonic 17 Quiff
18 Rampart 19 Stable 20 Tampan 21 Ungulate 22 Venetian
23 Welkin 24 Yabber

7–9   Fair
10–12   Good
13–16   Very good
17–24   Excellent

THIRTY-NINE

1 Alaska 2 Beef 3 Connolly 4 Desalination 5 Elba 6 Flanders
7 Gooseberry 8 Hughes 9 Incas 10 Jasper 11 Korea 12 Llasa
13 Moonlighting 14 Niagara 15 Opposite 16 Prokofiev
17 Quill 18 Riyadh 19 Sarajevo 20 Thrush 21 Ursula
22 Vocabulary 23 Watt 24 Yeltsin

7–9   Fair
10–12   Good
13–16   Very good
17–24   Excellent

FORTY

1 Aphrodite 2 Burnous 3 Croup 4 Duvet 5 Echinus 6 Faro
7 Genocide 8 Halser 9 Izzard 10 Jezebel 11 Kappa 12 Loure
13 Machismo 14 Noll 15 Onkus 16 Pulley 17 Quoin
18 Rand 19 Spinney 20 Tapir 21 Unicorn 22 Verbiage
23 Wensleydale 24 Yacca

7–9   Fair
10–12   Good
13–16   Very good
17–24   Excellent

FORTY-ONE

1 Adele 2 Blondel 3 Chinaman 4 Dennis 5 Eccles 6 Farouk
7 Graceland 8 Houston 9 India 10 Jerusalem 11 Kitchener
12 Liffey 13 Mussolini 14 Noses 15 Oberon 16 Player
17 Qatar 18 Roosevelt 19 Siege 20 Tonga 21 Ultramarine
22 Vertex 23 Woad 24 Zest

7–8   Fair
9–12   Good
13–16   Very good
17–24   Excellent

FORTY-TWO

1 Ashlar 2 Blarney 3 Cluster 4 Dromedary 5 Erudite
6 Farrago 7 Greenland 8 Hegira 9 Identikit 10 Jongleur
11 Kartel 12 Leone 13 Mackinan 14 Nopal 15 Opah
16 Poseidon 17 Quota 18 Rebuff 19 Skulk 20 Tonga
21 Ungula 22 Verboten 23 Wheatear 24 Yapok

7–8	Fair
9–12	Good
13–16	Very good
17–24	Excellent

FORTY-THREE

1 Aster 2 Birds 3 Cryptology 4 Drums 5 Eric 6 Forester
7 Glenn 8 Hepburn 9 Isherwood 10 Joe 11 Kerry 12 Lockjaw
13 Matthews 14 Noah 15 Ostrich 16 Prime 17 Quartz
18 Roget 19 Semibreve 20 Tiananmen 21 Urdu 22 Varlet
23 Wallis 24 Xylophone

7–8	Fair
9–12	Good
13–16	Very good
17–24	Excellent

FORTY-FOUR

1 Alto-cumulus 2 Bobalink 3 Calabash 4 Dressage
5 Espagnolette 6 Farrow 7 Graves 8 Heliology 9 Inchoate
10 Jeté 11 Khud 12 Lempira 13 Madeleine 14 Nardoo
15 Oloroso 16 Praline 17 Quirk 18 Regulo 19 Spring
20 Tong 21 Urceolus 22 Vesta 23 Wherry 24 Yapp

7–8	Fair
9–12	Good
13–16	Very good
17–24	Excellent

FORTY-FIVE

1 Aardvark 2 Blondin 3 Cagney 4 Diaper 5 Enigma 6 Farmer
7 Greenpeace 8 Hair 9 Isotherm 10 Jewellery 11 Kern
12 Lending 13 Malawi 14 Nixon 15 Oedipus 16 Pinter
17 Quantify 18 Revolver 19 Sirius 20 Tara 21 Upsilon
22 Veleta 23 Wombat 24 Zen

7–8	Fair
9–12	Good
13–16	Very good
17–24	Excellent

FORTY-SIX

1 Alicante 2 Bessemer 3 Clouds 4 Dragee 5 Esplanade
6 Fauteuil 7 Garnet 8 Hamilcar 9 Inkies 10 Judaism
11 Kerosene 12 Linus 13 Maffick 14 Neap 15 Oread
16 Prandial 17 Quoth 18 Réveillé 19 Sedge 20 Tauricide
21 Urubu 22 Veda 23 Whey 24 Yegg

7–8	Fair
9–12	Good
13–16	Very good
17–24	Excellent

FORTY-SEVEN

1 Antonym 2 Barabbas 3 Chekhov 4 Davenport 5 Electra
6 Fanlight 7 Gilbert 8 Hamelin 9 Issigonis 10 Jigger 11 Kama
12 Lambeth 13 McArthur 14 Neutron 15 Olivier 16 Parr
17 Quotient 18 Riddler 19 Speakeasy 20 Tennyson
21 Uruguay 22 Valance 23 Wildebeest 24 Zither

6–8	Fair
9–11	Good
12–15	Very good
16–24	Excellent

FORTY-EIGHT

1 Alopecia 2 Bissell 3 Cabriole 4 Dragoman 5 Estancia 6 Flea
7 Garbanzo 8 Hepplewhite 9 Icarus 10 Julian 11 Knitch
12 Leghorn 13 Maiden-hair 14 Naze 15 Orison 16 Prawn
17 Quadra 18 Revue 19 Siege 20 Tambour 21 Umbilical
22 Vole 23 Whig 24 Yojan

6–8	Fair
9–11	Good
12–15	Very good
16–24	Excellent

FORTY-NINE

1 Albatross 2 Brecht 3 Cabal 4 Dolittle 5 Ethics 6 Factorial
7 Griffin 8 Habitat 9 Implode 10 Jones 11 Kittyhawk
12 Luanda 13 Many 14 Nectarine 15 Ovett 16 Pravda
17 Quantas 18 Rosebery 19 Surtees 20 Truman
21 Ultrasonics 22 Vandyke 23 Windscale 24 Yalta

6–8	Fair
9–11	Good
12–15	Very good
16–24	Excellent

FIFTY

1 Ambergris 2 Bandolier 3 Columbine 4 Dermatology 5 Ethos
6 Fief 7 Guggenheim 8 Hammal 9 Icarian 10 Jack Straw
11 Koff 12 Leporide 13 Maize 14 Nonny 15 Orra 16 Precept
17 Quadrella 18 Rhomb 19 Sackbut 20 Taka 21 Umbraculum
22 Vibes 23 Whippet 24 Yttrium

6–8	Fair
9–11	Good
12–15	Very good
16–24	Excellent

FIFTY-ONE

1 Attorney 2 Benin 3 Christmas 4 Dimaggio 5 Endeavour
6 Four 7 Gregory 8 Hawaii 9 Infanta 10 Jung 11 Kittens
12 Longchamps 13 Manny 14 Naseby 15 Occident
16 Porcelain 17 Quantum 18 Rufus 19 Spectre 20 Typefaces
21 Urals 22 Viscid 23 Wagons 24 Yangtze

6–8	Fair
9–11	Good
12–15	Very good
16–24	Excellent

FIFTY-TWO

1 Acolyte 2 Baldric 3 Coracle 4 Dodecahedron 5 Escalope
6 Frog 7 Gusli 8 Hammam 9 Impresario 10 Jackaroo
11 Kumquat 12 Laudanum 13 Mammock 14 Nunatak
15 Oscan 16 Précis 17 Quacksalver 18 Riprap 19 Sleuth
20 Timbale 21 Umbrette 22 Viking 23 Widget 24 Yulan

6–8	Fair
9–11	Good
12–15	Very good
16–24	Excellent

FIFTY-THREE

1 Atacama 2 Bonanza 3 Casanova 4 Diabolo 5 Eusebio
6 Fatima 7 Graceful 8 Hovercraft 9 Images 10 Jasper 11 Krill
12 Lerner 13 Magyar 14 Narcissus 15 Offenbach 16 Pepys
17 Quarto 18 Rollmop 19 Satsuma 20 Topiary 21 Utrillo
22 Vestibule 23 Woolworth 24 Younger

6–8	Fair
9–11	Good
12–15	Very good
16–24	Excellent

FIFTY-FOUR

1 Aubergine   2 Baht   3 Colonnade   4 Dexter   5 Edentate   6 Fossa
7 Gynophobia   8 Hairy   9 Incus   10 Jaeger   11 Kyle
12 Laureate   13 Manatee   14 Noyall   15 Ovicide   16 Pretzel
17 Quadrifid   18 Rayful   19 Satsuma   20 Taurine
21 Ulotrichous   22 Viniculture   23 Willet   24 Yeld

6–8	Fair
9–11	Good
12–15	Very good
16–24	Excellent

FIFTY-FIVE

1 Andropov   2 Brittain   3 Constellations   4 Drey   5 Equinox
6 Furlough   7 Guidebook   8 Humphreys   9 Igneous
10 Jerusalem   11 Kalahari   12 Liberace   13 Money   14 Namibia
15 Onassis   16 Pluto   17 Quinsy   18 Rubber   19 Svengali
20 Transvaal   21 Unleavened   22 Vernal   23 Weatherfield
24 Xenon

6–8	Fair
9–11	Good
12–15	Very good
16–24	Excellent

FIFTY-SIX

1 Abatis   2 Building   3 Cassata   4 Dervish   5 Ecology   6 Fondant
7 Greaves   8 Haggis   9 Ingenue   10 Jalousie   11 Kiang   12 Levée
13 Mandible   14 Nitid   15 Oliphant   16 Procyon   17 Quaestor
18 Rachel   19 State   20 Tetradi   21 Uliginose   22 Vixen
23 Winnow   24 Ypsilon

6–8	Fair
9–11	Good
12–15	Very good
16–24	Excellent

FIFTY-SEVEN

1 Aeroflot 2 Balaclava 3 Crapper 4 Douglas 5 Esperanto
6 Firkin 7 Gully 8 Havel 9 Islam 10 Juggernaut 11 Kampala
12 Leviticus 13 Mollison 14 Nippon 15 Octahedron
16 Prayers 17 Quiver 18 Rabat 19 Solstice 20 Twain
21 Usurp 22 Vespers 23 Weissmuller 24 Yarn

5–8	Fair
9–10	Good
11–14	Very good
15–24	Excellent

FIFTY-EIGHT

1 Abele 2 Baffy 3 Conchoid 4 Donjon 5 Elegy 6 Fogle 7 Grist
8 Haha 9 Intaglio 10 Jardinière 11 Kelpie 12 Lectern
13 Mansard 14 Nis 15 Ornithology 16 Pula 17 Quebracho
18 Racon 19 Smuck 20 Tugrik 21 Uhlan 22 Valencia
23 Wiseacre 24 Yowley

5–8	Fair
9–10	Good
11–14	Very good
15–24	Excellent

FIFTY-NINE

1 Arches 2 Bullet 3 Chatsworth 4 Denning 5 Emitting
6 Firedamp 7 Gum 8 Helen 9 Insects 10 Jungle 11 Karachi
12 Lindburgh 13 Manhattan 14 Nowel 15 Orcadian 16 Poets
17 Quasar 18 Reggae 19 Starfish 20 Ticktack 21 Ufology
22 Vostok 23 Wedge 24 Yorktown

5–8	Fair
9–10	Good
11–14	Very good
15–24	Excellent

SIXTY

1 Afghani 2 Brindisi 3 Campanology 4 Dolce 5 Eringo
6 Firebreak 7 Gemshorn 8 Haboob 9 Intercostal 10 Journology
11 Kebbuck 12 Lippy 13 Manumit 14 Noctograph
15 Observance 16 Parallelepipedon 17 Quadrifoliate 18 Racloir
19 Stager 20 Tilak 21 Upal 22 Vortex 23 Wahine 24 Yemen

5–8	Fair
9–10	Good
11–14	Very good
15–24	Excellent

SIXTY-ONE

1 Alliteration 2 Bat 3 Cyan 4 Davidson 5 Eagle 6 Ferris
7 Glasnost 8 Hudson 9 Imogen 10 Jellyfish 11 Kerosene
12 Low 13 Malcolm 14 Numbers 15 Odyssey 16 Perfect
17 Quid 18 Robinson 19 Surplice 20 Tachograph 21 Upbraid
22 Vernier 23 William 24 Xerxes

5–7	Fair
8–10	Good
11–14	Very good
15–24	Excellent

SIXTY-TWO

1 Aorta 2 Business 3 Cedi 4 Dolose 5 Etiolate 6 Fitch
7 Gourde 8 Huygens 9 Isanthous 10 Jumbuck 11 Kheda
12 Larrup 13 Mantology 14 Nelli 15 Ottavine 16 Phebology
17 Quahaug 18 Rackarock 19 Simplicity 20 Tonada
21 Uberty 22 Vulcan 23 Wairepo 24 Yarrah

5–7	Fair
8–10	.Good
11–14	Very good
15–24	Excellent

SIXTY-THREE

1 Alabaster 2 Batista 3 Cameroon 4 Dehavilland 5 Eastman
6 Fuller 7 Goodman 8 Hell 9 Isinglass 10 Jester 11 Keystone
12 Littlewoods 13 Moonshine 14 Novello 15 Oysters
16 Parkhurst 17 Quintessence 18 Robespierre 19 Skegness
20 Theseus 21 Ullage 22 Verso 23 Walton 24 Yates

5–7	Fair
8–10	Good
11–14	Very good
15–24	Excellent

SIXTY-FOUR

1 Abalone 2 Barren 3 Caucus 4 Dugong 5 Estrade 6 Fissiped
7 Godown 8 Hautboy 9 Isabel 10 Jabiru 11 Kibitka
12 Liquorice 13 Markka 14 Nephrectomy 15 Obang
16 Philippic 17 Quamash 18 Rabot 19 Sarangi 20 Thetis
21 Ubermensch 22 Vulparine 23 Waldhorn 24 Yawl

5–7	Fair
8–10	Good
11–14	Very good
15–24	Excellent

SIXTY-FIVE

1 Alderney 2 Barrymore 3 Celtic 4 Dresden 5 Ebony
6 Fillmore 7 Goldwyn 8 Hectolitre 9 Innocent 10 Jugglers
11 Kinetic 12 Lazarus 13 Myanmar 14 Nesbit 15 Onyx
16 Persia 17 Quitch 18 Reagan 19 Sword 20 Troilus
21 Uppsala 22 Vesper 23 Worship 24 Young

5–7	Fair
8–10	Good
11–14	Very good
15–24	Excellent

SIXTY-SIX

1 Austral 2 Blush 3 Collie 4 Duomo 5 Eidolon 6 Fiord
7 Gerontology 8 Hepatology 9 Isodont 10 Jacane 11 Kinchin
12 Lough 13 Mysophobia 14 Navicular 15 Obol
16 Pendragon 17 Quandog 18 Riel 19 Spelter 20 Tarocchi
21 Uffizi 22 Vivian 23 Wampee 24 Zebub

5–7	Fair
8–10	Good
11–14	Very good
15–24	Excellent

SIXTY-SEVEN

1 Arlington 2 Baseball 3 Cantabile 4 Digitalis 5 Egyptian
6 Forests 7 Gridiron 8 Humidity 9 Izvestia 10 Joyce 11 Koala
12 Leander 13 Miriam 14 Newgate 15 Orwell 16 Paparazzi
17 Quadragesima 18 Reuter 19 Saddles 20 *Tigris* 21 Urania
22 Velocipede 23 Washington 24 Zebedee

5–7	Fair
8–10	Good
11–14	Very good
15–24	Excellent

SIXTY-EIGHT

1 Arquebus 2 Burin 3 Caldera 4 Durbar 5 Eglantine 6 Finnan
7 Ghana 8 Hypnophobia 9 Intestacy 10 Jota 11 Kyat
12 Leister 13 Mikado 14 Nocturne 15 Oftel 16 Pizarro
17 Quarl 18 Rebec 19 Spinach 20 Thurible 21 Uropygium
22 Voltaire 23 Wapacut 24 Zareba

5–7	Fair
8–10	Good
11–14	Very good
15–24	Excellent

SIXTY-NINE

1 Archer 2 Bhutan 3 Cotton 4 *Dragnet* 5 Elysée 6 Fingal's
7 Grahame 8 Hieroglyphics 9 Ira 10 John 11 Kowloon
12 Lombard 13 Magenta 14 Nash 15 Orlando 16 Parkinson's
17 Quod 18 Richards 19 Stoppard 20 Tirana 21 Unciform
22 Vaporetto 23 Waugh 24 Zeus

5–7	Fair
8–10	Good
11–14	Very good
15–24	Excellent

SEVENTY

1 Aglet 2 Berceuse 3 Cwms 4 Duppy 5 Eremology 6 Fink
7 Galette 8 Husk 9 Invar 10 Jaguarundi 11 Kwanza
12 Leprechaun 13 Mononucleosis 14 Newton 15 Ohone
16 Praxis 17 Quintal 18 Rufiyaa 19 Squid 20 Thrasonigal
21 Uranology 22 Vulsella 23 Wishtonwish 24 Zap

5–7	Fair
8–10	Good
11–14	Very good
15–24	Excellent

SEVENTY-ONE

1 Ashley 2 Beermats 3 Cowdray 4 Debrett's 5 Epics 6 Firefly
7 Guillotin 8 Helium 9 Infinity 10 Japan 11 Kruger 12 Lakes
13 Mycroft 14 Newspeak 15 Oratory 16 Pear 17 Quietism
18 Reflexology 19 Selfridge 20 Telstar 21 Udometer
22 Valediction 23 Waikiki 24 Zermatt

4–6	Fair
7–9	Good
10–13	Very good
14–24	Excellent

SEVENTY-TWO

1 Amorphous 2 Baccate 3 Cerberus 4 Dudeen 5 Emissary
6 Fillip 7 Galleon 8 Hybrid 9 Iracund 10 Jansky
11 Kyphophobia 12 Lederhosen 13 Montague 14 Nestor
15 Omadhaun 16 Predial 17 Quassia 18 Rheic 19 Suez
20 Thalassophobia 21 Underwing 22 Volant 23 Wistiti
24 Zamouse

4–6	Fair
7–9	Good
10–13	Very good
14–24	Excellent

SEVENTY-THREE

1 Asimov 2 Buchan 3 Calvary 4 Dillinger 5 Equamons
6 Fisher 7 Galápagos 8 Hardy 9 Iran 10 Jars 11 Kelvin
12 Larboard 13 Mice 14 Nazarite 15 Osprey 16 Peary
17 Quartan 18 Romney 19 Surgeon 20 Thurber
21 Unification 22 Vitriol 23 Wasps 24 Zebu

4–6	Fair
7–9	Good
10–13	Very good
14–24	Excellent

SEVENTY-FOUR

1 Assemblage 2 Barrico 3 Cetology 4 Drow 5 Embouchure
6 Filibuster 7 Guyana 8 Hooghly 9 Isiac 10 Jura 11 Kalology
12 Lathi 13 Marimba 14 Nainsook 15 Omasum 16 Princock
17 Quickthorn 18 Repertoire 19 Selenology 20 Tancred
21 Ugli 22 Vitrine 23 Wirrycow 24 Zakuska

4–6	Fair
7–9	Good
10–13	Very good
14–24	Excellent

144

SEVENTY-FIVE

1 Amethyst 2 Branwell 3 Cauthen 4 Dredge 5 Equity
6 Farrier 7 Gabon 8 Horn 9 Isadora 10 Julian 11 Kibbutz
12 Lollards 13 McCarthyism 14 Nemesis 15 Oceania 16 Paris
17 Quatrain 18 Rubella 19 Stipendiary 20 Trollope 21 Usance
22 Virago 23 Wagtail 24 Zatopek

4–6	Fair
7–9	Good
10–13	Very good
14–24	Excellent

SEVENTY-SIX

1 Acajou 2 Bactrian 3 Cakewalk 4 Drupe 5 Ebenezer 6 Filial
7 Galligaskins 8 Hypogeal 9 Itinerant 10 Jataka
11 Koniphobia 12 Leporicide 13 Mekong 14 Naja 15 Oleic
16 Proa 17 Quenelle 18 Recreant 19 Sacology 20 Taberdar
21 Unbraid 22 Virgule 23 Winze 24 Zabaglione

4–6	Fair
7–9	Good
10–13	Very good
14–24	Excellent

SEVENTY-SEVEN

1 *Amadeus* 2 Brimstone 3 Coney 4 Decimation 5 Estonia
6 Fontainebleau 7 Geothermal 8 Harpsichord 9 Ibsen
10 Jocasta 11 Kidderminster 12 La Guardia 13 Muted
14 Newel 15 Opus 16 Perigee 17 Quadraphonic 18 Robey
19 Savoy 20 Tercentenary 21 Urry 22 Varicella 23 Winds
24 Xenophobia

4–6	Fair
7–9	Good
10–13	Very good
14–24	Excellent

SEVENTY-EIGHT

1 Ancipital 2 Bury 3 Cortez 4 Drammock 5 Eclogue 6 Filar
7 Galliwasp 8 Haaf 9 Izard 10 Jarvey 11 Kwacha
12 Lithology 13 Marchpane 14 Nandine 15 Olid 16 Praetor
17 Quercus 18 Rangoon 19 Sucre 20 Tablature 21 Ursuline
22 Vimana 23 Wapper 24 Zoic

4–6	Fair
7–9	Good
10–13	Very good
14–24	Excellent

SEVENTY-NINE

1 Alitalia 2 Beeton 3 Crocodile 4 Daphne 5 Everest 6 Fiscal
7 Greer 8 Heartbeat 9 Incandescent 10 Jade 11 Kieran
12 Linen 13 Microcosm 14 Nissen 15 Orpheus 16 Pessimists
17 Quixotic 18 Raffles 19 Saigon 20 Tarragon 21 Unicorn
22 Vulgate 23 Walrus 24 Zircon

4–6	Fair
7–9	Good
10–13	Very good
14–24	Excellent

EIGHTY

1 Ancon 2 Bevy 3 Czardas 4 Dalasi 5 Ensiform 6 Filasse
7 Galoot 8 Habanera 9 Inutile 10 Jargonelle 11 Katharina
12 La volta 13 Mannequin 14 Nannygal 15 Oligopod
16 Peavey 17 Querl 18 Razoo 19 Sute 20 Tach 21 Urticaria
22 Vigia 23 Wayzgoose 24 Zymosis

4–6	Fair
7–9	Good
10–13	Very good
14–24	Excellent

EIGHTY-ONE

1 Atatürk 2 Butcher 3 Clay 4 Dukakis 5 Elysium 6 Fool's
7 Goossens 8 Hiccups 9 Istanbul 10 Jeroboam 11 Kaleidoscope
12 Longships 13 Morpheus 14 Nerves 15 Ocelot 16 Pins
17 Quadrille 18 Raleigh 19 Swan 20 Terpsichorean
21 Unbundle 22 Veronique 23 Words 24 Zambezi

4–5	Fair
6–8	Good
9–12	Very good
13–24	Excellent

EIGHTY-TWO

1 Accelerando 2 Blast 3 Cruzacio 4 Donga 5 Eyre 6 Fidibus
7 Galumph 8 Hackamore 9 Ibidem 10 Jampan 11 Kabuki
12 Linonophobia 13 Manchineel 14 Nartijie 15 Olitory
16 Powell 17 Quine 18 Rathaus 19 Subtrahend 20 Tyr
21 Uniliteral 22 Vestiary 23 Weem 24 Zog

4–5	Fair
6–8	Good
9–12	Very good
13–24	Excellent

EIGHTY-THREE

1 Akihito 2 Borden 3 Cakes 4 Decalogue 5 Eggs 6 Ferret
7 Geodesic 8 Hiawatha 9 Insects 10 Jabberwocky 11 Knesset
12 Lizard 13 Mint 14 Noriega 15 Octingenary 16 Pickles
17 Queue 18 Rural 19 Summation 20 Taupin 21 Upcast
22 Vanderbilt 23 Winter 24 Zoolatry

4–5	Fair
6–8	Good
9–12	Very good
13–24	Excellent

1 Azoic 2 Balbao 3 Cachucha 4 Dendrology 5 Exon 5 Flemish
7 Gamash 8 Hadji 9 Ichthyic 10 Jannock 11 Kadjibut
12 Ländler 13 Malkin 14 Noisette 15 Organdie
16 Psychometer 17 Quibble 18 Ratapian 19 Strabismic
20 Tahini 21 Umquhile 22 Veronica 23 Wentletrap
24 Zanzibar

4–5	Fair
6–8	Good
9–12	Very good
13–24	Excellent

EIGHTY-FIVE

1 Aniseed 2 Bolas 3 Claudius 4 Dogs 5 Elections 6 Forum
7 Gaumont 8 Hispaniola 9 Invar 10 Joanna 11 Kandy
12 Lansbury 13 Matchboxes 14 Nautilus 15 Osmium
16 Pangram 17 Quindecagon 18 Rorschach 19 Sikorsky
20 Terylene 21 Urubu 22 Vaquero 23 Warbeck 24 Zeiss

4–5	Fair
6–8	Good
9–12	Very good
13–24	Excellent

EIGHTY-SIX

1 Acephalous 2 Baguette 3 Cordoba 4 Dirge 5 Epiphyte
6 Fiacre 7 Grannon 8 Haka 9 Ideophobia 10 Jambeaux
11 Kae 12 Lucy 13 Malar 14 Nuphar 15 Ombre
16 Peloponnesia 17 Quillet 18 Rapscallion 19 Salicet
20 Talaha 21 Umbles 22 Verglas 23 Whaup 24 Zapateado

4–5	Fair
6–8	Good
9–12	Very good
13–24	Excellent

EIGHTY-SEVEN

1 Auden 2 Beauvis 3 Colours 4 Droshky 5 Entebbe 6 Fishing
7 Gallup 8 Huntingdon 9 Icosahedron 10 Jardinière 11 Kendo
12 Leofric 13 Martingale 14 Nikkei 15 Obelisk 16 Pascal
17 Quagga 18 Rockefeller 19 Seraphim 20 Tasmania
21 Univalve 22 Volstead 23 Wars 24 Zebrine

4–5	Fair
6–8	Good
9–11	Very good
12–24	Excellent

EIGHTY-EIGHT

1 Arak 2 Brontophobia 3 Conchology 4 Drift 5 Escadrille
6 Fibular 7 Gaikwar 8 Hakeem 9 Intrados 10 Jambalaya
11 Kago 12 Linnet 13 Maillot 14 Nylghau 15 Omerta
16 Phon 17 Quarrel 18 Ramulose 19 Shrewdness 20 Takapu
21 Utas 22 Vedette 23 Whidah 24 Young

4–5	Fair
6–8	Good
9–11	Very good
12–24	Excellent

EIGHTY-NINE

1 Advertising 2 Brezhnev 3 Charon 4 Dirt 5 Eigg 6 Fez
7 Goshen 8 Hectogram 9 Iridescent 10 Jewel 11 Ketch
12 Lippmann 13 Machete 14 Nirvana 15 Occluded
16 Pollyanna 17 Quincunx 18 Raphael 19 Star 20 Trudeau
21 Upas 22 Vigorously 23 Wine 24 Zechariah

4–5	Fair
6–8	Good
9–11	Very good
12–24	Excellent

NINETY

1 Ampula 2 Badelynge 3 Coolah 4 Diet 5 Evangelists 6 Fictile
7 Galago 8 Haloid 9 Impeyan 10 Jai-alai 11 Kama
12 Lusitania 13 Maga 14 Nutria 15 Omohyoid 16 Pataca
17 Quinquina 18 Ramshackle 19 Sesquiplicate 20 Talipot
21 Ustion 22 Voe 23 Whin 24 Zaire

4–5	Fair
6–8	Good
9–11	Very good
12–24	Excellent

NINETY-ONE

1 Alcohol 2 Boar 3 Crosses 4 Diefenbaker 5 Eyelids
6 Fingerprints 7 Ghandi 8 Hughes 9 Injustice 10 Jesse
11 Khmer 12 Luxair 13 Matilda 14 Nymphs 15 Oxbow
16 Postcards 17 Quittal 18 Realtor 19 Sapper 20 Thunder
21 Uzbekistan 22 Vermillion 23 Wood 24 Ziggurat

3–4	Fair
5–7	Good
8–10	Very good
11–24	Excellent

NINETY-TWO

1 Aliped 2 Batophobia 3 Chaparrel 4 Distich 5 Eruciform
6 Fichu 7 Gadwall 8 Halyard 9 Inanga 10 Jacquerie
11 Kilderkin 12 Logopedics 13 Maduro 14 Nisei
15 Omophagic 16 Pelcatophobia 17 Quintic 18 Rameous
19 Sheraton 20 Tamasha 21 Urus 22 Vasculum 23 Whisket
24 Xantippe

3–4	Fair
5–7	Good
8–10	Very good
11–24	Excellent

NINETY-THREE

1 Atlantis 2 Boot 3 Crowds 4 Dolly 5 Eyot 6 Fruits
7 Goatsbeard 8 Heart 9 Iridium 10 Jugal 11 Kraft
12 Loneliness 13 Misericord 14 Nyasa 15 Occiput 16 Pershing
17 Quinquennium 18 Rainfall 19 Slade 20 Titicaca
21 Univocalic 22 Vulcanology 23 Whistler 24 Yamamoto

3–4	Fair
5–7	Good
8–10	Very good
11–24	Excellent

NINETY-FOUR

1 Alvine 2 Blackbeard 3 Cymophobia 4 Dirham
5 Emmenthaler 6 Figuline 7 Gaby 8 Hamadryad 9 Infula
10 Jacobus 11 Kippage 12 Lemuel 13 Macula 14 Nimiety
15 Omoplate 16 Parterre 17 Quodlibet 18 Ramekin
19 Soothsayer 20 Tanager 21 Undertakers 22 Variola
23 Whortleberry 24 Xenelasia

3–4	Fair
5–7	Good
8–10	Very good
11–24	Excellent

NINETY-FIVE

1 Argus 2 Bellingham 3 Cromwell 4 Devil's 5 Ergophobia
6 Flowers 7 Gargoyles 8 Hyperbole 9 Ironbridge 10 Judogi
12 Kepler 12 Languages 13 Mossad 14 Narnia 15 Orlando
16 Poppaea 17 Quadriga 18 Ricin 19 Speed 20 Tuvalu
21 Uxoricide 22 Viviparity 23 Wool 24 Zirconium

3–4	Fair
5–7	Good
8–10	Very good
11–24	Excellent

NINETY-SIX

1 Aliform 2 Batrachophobe 3 Cantatrice 4 Dasymeter
5 Equipedal 6 Foumant 7 Gaberfunzie 8 Hamate 9 Ink/slinger
10 Jacchus 11 Kistvaen 12 Laager 13 Macron 14 Noachian
15 Oopak 16 Ponticello 17 Quesadilla 18 Rame 19 Scutiform
20 Tanrec 21 Uraeous 22 Vallum 23 Wicken 24 Xenogamy

3–4	Fair
5–7	Good
8–10	Very good
11–24	Excellent

NINETY-SEVEN

1 Aylward 2 Blushing 3 Cellophane 4 Dark 5 Europa
6 Filibuster 7 Glass 8 Hotspur 9 Irving 10 Jurisprudence
11 Kiribati 12 Lying 13 Mosses 14 Napier 15 Orly
16 Peacock 17 Quirt 18 Retinol 19 Sausage 20 Tiffany
21 Ustion 22 Valetudinarian 23 Warwick 24 Yahoos

3–4	Fair
5–7	Good
8–9	Very good
10–24	Excellent

NINETY-EIGHT

1 Anechoic 2 Babouche 3 Clinophobia 4 Dotterel 5 Exurbia
6 Fortalice 7 Gabelle 8 Hidrosis 9 Inquiling 10 Jaal 11 Kloof
12 Lapilli 13 Moorstone 14 Noctule 15 Ovolo 16 Phyllophobe
17 Quaternion 18 Radicchio 19 Siphonapterologist 20 Tapis
21 Ulmaceous 22 Vallecula 23 Wiener 24 Xenomania

3–4	Fair
5–7	Good
8–9	Very good
10–24	Excellent